Heroes
in
American
Folklore

ILLUSTRATED

BY

JAMES DAUGHERTY

AND

DONALD McKAY

Heroes in American Folklore

BY

IRWIN SHAPIRO

JULIAN MESSNER, INC.

New York

Published by Julian Messner, Inc.
8 West 40 Street, New York 18

Published simultaneously in Canada
by The Copp Clark Publishing Co. Limited

CONTENTS

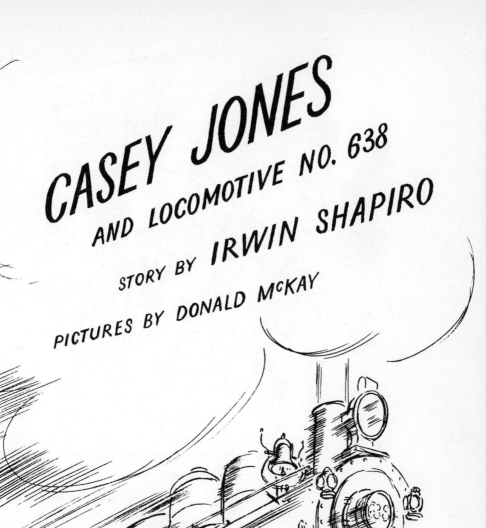

CASEY JONES
AND LOCOMOTIVE NO. 638

STORY BY IRWIN SHAPIRO

PICTURES BY DONALD McKAY

THERE's always been a Jones on the railroad. And the greatest of them all was Casey Jones.

Casey couldn't help being a railroad man. He was born to the long, lonesome wail of a locomotive whistle. He grew up to the sound of the engine moan. He started out as a call boy, then was a ticket agent, a telegraph operator, a brakeman, and a fireman. At last he got to be an engineer, and drove a big eight-wheeler of a mighty fame.

Yes, everybody knows Casey was a great engineer. Everybody knows the song about Casey. Everybody *doesn't* know that the song jumps the track when it says Casey was killed in the wreck of Locomotive No. 638. Because the truth is, there wasn't any wreck. The truth is, Casey almost didn't even get near No. 638. The truth is that Casey liked to play baseball, and—well, here's what really happened.

8

It all goes back to the day the east-bound limited was
rolling along toward Chicago. Casey was sitting in the cab
of Locomotive No. 4. He was wearing high-bibbed overalls
and a red thousand-mile shirt. He had a black engineer's
cap on his head, and a blue bandanna handkerchief around
his neck for a sweat rag.

As they rattled over a crossing, Casey checked the time on
his gold stem-winding watch. After that he picked up his
long-necked copper oil can and put a drop of oil on his
handle-bar mustache.

"Nothing like a little prime, pure en-jine oil to give
whiskers a gloss," he said to the fireman.

Pulling into the depot at Chicago, Casey played his
whippoorwill call on the whistle. And when he did, the folks
at the depot stopped whatever they were doing. The bag-
gage-smashers stopped handling baggage. The telegraph

9

operators stopped pounding brass. The station agent stopped selling tickets, and the passengers stopped buying tickets. For they knew the man at the throttle was Casey Jones.

A crowd of Joneses came rushing up to the locomotive. With them was Casey's uncle, old Memphis Jones. Uncle Memphis had been an engineer himself, and he still wore a black engineer's cap. At the end of every run he was always on hand with a crowd of other Joneses to give Casey a cheer.

"There he is!" said Uncle Memphis proudly.

"Hurray for Casey!" shouted the Joneses. "Hurray for Casey Jones!"

Casey swung himself off the cab, giving the crowd a wave of the hand.

"How's the old pitching arm?" asked Uncle Memphis.

"Strong and limber and ready to pitch," answered Casey.

"How about showing us your new razzle-dazzler?" said the Joneses.

"Glad to obleege," said Casey.

Uncle Memphis handed Casey a baseball and a pitcher's glove. He stood off from Casey, put on a catcher's mitt, and gave Casey the signal. Casey wound up and let the ball fly.

The ball swung out in a big curve. Then it took three little hops. Then it twisted around like a corkscrew, and bam! hit the catcher's mitt.

"That's pitching!" yelled the Joneses. "Sure is a razzle-dazzler!"

"Baseball—hm!" said a deep voice behind Casey, and Casey turned around.

There stood a little fat man with bushy eyebrows. He was wearing a derby hat and a stand-up collar. He had a diamond stick-pin in his tie, and he was carrying a gold-handled cane.

"Well, well," said Casey. "If it's not Bolsun Brown, Superintendent of the Central Pacific Railroad."

Before Bolsun could open his mouth to speak, Casey held up his hand.

"Same old Bolsun," said Casey. "First thing you'll do is tell me it doesn't look right to pitch ball on the platform of the depot."

Bolsun tapped his cane on the ground. But he didn't say a word.

"After that," said Casey, "you'll tell me it doesn't look right for an engineer to play baseball."

Once again Bolsun didn't say a word.

"Then," said Casey, "you'll tell me baseball and railroading don't mix."

Still Bolsun didn't say a word.

"And you'll end up," said Casey, "by telling me I ought to give up baseball. And if I don't, I'll lose my touch on the throttle."

Bolsun cleared his throat and said, "Casey, it's true it doesn't look right for you to play baseball. But I'm not saying so. It's true baseball and railroading don't mix. But I'm not saying that, either. It's true you ought to give it up, and it's true you'll lose your touch on the throttle. But that's something else I'm not saying."

Casey looked at Bolsun.

"Maybe it's not the same old Bolsun after all," he said. "You sure you're not going to say any ot those things?"

"Not one," said Bolsun. "All I've got to say is this— I'd like to show you something at the World's Fair Exposition."

Casey asked Uncle Memphis if there was anything at the Exposition for a railroad man to see.

"Couldn't say," answered Uncle Memphis. "I haven't had time to go there. I haven't even read about it in the paper. I've been too busy working out the batting averages of your baseball team."

"Guess it won't do any harm to take a look at it," said Casey, and the three of them left the depot.

It was evening when they got to the Exposition grounds. Crowds of people walked between the white buildings. Colored lights were strung everywhere. Fountains spurted. Gondolas floated on the big lake. Bands played music, and fireworks exploded in the sky.

The Midway of the Exposition was lined with the tents of side-shows. Barkers shouted, "R-r-r-right this way, folks! The big show is about to begin! Don't miss it! Only ten cents—one dime—the tenth part of a dollar. Hurry, hurry, hurry!"

But Bolsun wouldn't let Casey and Uncle Memphis see the side-shows. He wouldn't let them see the sword swallower,

the midgets, or the human skeleton. He hustled them straight to a big white building, with a golden arch and golden letters that said:

HALL OF TRANSPORTATION

Inside the building, Bolsun pulled them away from an old Stevenson locomotive and a bright new Pullman car.

"That's not what I wanted to show you," he said. Then he pointed with his gold-handled cane and said, "But *that* is."

On a little spur of track stood a new locomotive. She was a big eight-wheeler, the biggest ever built. She had the longest

driving-rod ever made. Her black paint was as dark as the inside of a tunnel, and her brass bell shone like a light. She was decked out in flags and red-white-and-blue bunting. Propped up against her was a sign:

LOCOMOTIVE NO. 638

Built on the order
of
Superintendent Bolsun Brown
for the
CENTRAL PACIFIC RAILROAD

Casey walked all around No. 638. He looked her over, and he looked her under, and he looked her every which way.

"That *is* a smokeolotive," he said.

"I'm not denying it," said Bolsun.

"That is a hog," said Uncle Memphis.

"I'm not disputing it," said Bolsun.

"Makes old No. 4 look like a hay-burner," said Casey.

"I'm not saying she doesn't," said Bolsun.

Bolsun leaned back on his gold-handled cane.

"Casey," he said, "how would you like to put your hand on her throttle? How would you like to play your whippoorwill call on her whistle? How would you like to sit in her cab and watch her drivers roll?"

"I can see her now," said Casey, "highballing along, breaking all records. I can see her now."

"Casey," said Bolsun quickly, "you give up baseball, and I'll let you take out No. 638. I'll give you the right-of-way from Chicago to 'Frisco, and you can break all records."

"Why, Bolsun," said Uncle Memphis, "you couldn't

17

give No. 638 to anybody *else*. Nobody but a Jones could handle her, and Casey's the only Jones on the railroad."

"I don't know about that," said Bolsun. "A Brown could handle her. I used to be an engineer myself, and I'd take the run if I wasn't Superintendent."

Casey and Uncle Memphis burst out laughing. Uncle Memphis snorted and said, "Bolsun, you're a good Superintendent. But you never were much of an engineer. Casey is the only man around to take out No. 638. You'll never get him to give up baseball that way."

"Just a minute," said Casey. "I'd like to obleege you, Bolsun. And I'd like to take out No. 638. I'll tell you what I'll do; if my baseball team loses the game next week, I'll give up baseball."

"But your team never loses," said Bolsun, frowning. "You know—"

Suddenly Bolsun stopped. He walked a few steps up and down, tapping with his gold-handled cane. Then the frown left his face and he held out his hand.

"I'll take you up on that," he said. "If your team loses, you'll give up baseball. And I'll give you the right-of-way to 'Frisco with No. 638."

"Don't do it, Casey!" shouted Uncle Memphis. "Don't

take him up on it! He's got some trick thought up to make you lose the game!"

"The only trick he could do," said Casey, "is to find the other team a pitcher like me. But there's only one Casey Jones. I'll take you up on that, Bolsun."

Bolsun and Casey shook hands. They had another look at No. 638, then left the Exposition grounds together. Bolsun went to his house, and Casey and Uncle Memphis went to their rooms at Mrs. Callahan's Rooming House for Railroad men.

All that week Casey took out old No. 4. The day of the game he brought her into the depot the way he always did. He put a drop of engine oil on his handle-bar mustache to give it a gloss, and headed straight for the ball park.

Soon as Casey came out on the field, his catcher said, "You're just in time. Better get into your uniform and warm up."

"I don't need any uniform," said Casey. "And I don't

need to warm up. My arm is still warm from en-jine heat."

The next minute the umpire held up his hand.

"Bat-tries for today's game!" he shouted, "For Casey Jones's Tigers—Casey Jones and Smith! For the South Side Wildcats—Hallahan and Hoke! Play ball!"

Casey walked out to the pitcher's mound, while the folks gave him a cheer. On one side of the stands sat the Wildcat rooters. On the other side sat the Tiger rooters. With them was Uncle Memphis, and almost every Jones in the city of Chicago. And sitting squeezed in between the Wildcat rooters and the Tiger rooters was Bolsun Brown.

"Let's go!" cried the Tiger rooters. "Give 'em the old razzle-dazzler, Casey!"

"Come on, you Wildcats!" said the Wildcat rooters. "Knock Casey out of the box!"

Bolsun Brown didn't cheer with the Tigers or the Wildcats. He just sat there, watching Casey from under his bushy eyebrows. His hands were folded over his gold-handled cane, and his chin rested on his hands.

"Batter up!" shouted the umpire, and the game was on.

The first seven innings, Casey didn't allow the Wildcats a hit. He made three home runs himself, scoring two men. The score was five to nothing, favor the Tigers.

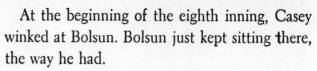

At the beginning of the eighth inning, Casey winked at Bolsun. Bolsun just kept sitting there, the way he had.

"I knew Bolsun couldn't keep me from winning," said Casey to himself. He got the signal from the catcher, wound up, and threw a curve.

"Stur-r-r-r-i-i-ike!" said the umpire.

Casey got the ball again and threw a straight fast one.

"Ball!" said the umpire.

The batter missed Casey's next pitch by a mile.

"Strike tuh!" said the umpire.

The pitch after that was a little close.

"Ball tuh!" said the umpire. "Tuh and tuh!"

The next two were high and a little wide.

"Ball thu-ree!" said the umpire. "Thu-ree and tuh! Thu-ree and tuh!"

The catcher tossed the ball to the first baseman. The first baseman tossed it to the second baseman. The second baseman tossed it to the shortstop. The shortstop tossed it to the third baseman, who tossed it to the catcher. The catcher

walked over to Casey and handed him the ball. Before he went back behind the plate, he whispered something in Casey's ear. Casey whispered something back and nodded.

"Take him out!" yelled the Wildcat rooters. "He's up in the air! He's up in the air!"

"Give him the old razzle-dazzler, Casey!" yelled the Tiger rooters. "Strike him out!"

"Play ball!" said the umpire.

Casey leaned way back, wound way up, and let the ball fly. First it swung out in a big curve. Then it took three little hops. Then it twisted around like a corkscrew, and bam! hit the catcher's mitt.

"Ball!" said the umpire. "Ball four! Take ya base!"

"Boo!" said the Tiger rooters. "Robber! Blind man! Get him a tin cup!"

Before the batter could even throw down his bat, Bolsun Brown hopped out of the stands. He waved his gold-handled cane in the air. He jumped up and down. And he ran out on the field, bellowing, "What's that you said, umpire?"

"Ball four," said the umpire.

"Why, you wall-eyed swindler!" roared Bolsun. "That ball was right over the plate!"

Both teams came crowding around Bolsun and the umpire. Everybody except Casey was talking and shouting and waving his hands.

Bolsun pushed Casey close to the umpire.

"Go ahead, Casey!" he yelled. "Tell him! Tell this blind man!"

23

"Just what are you going to tell me?" the umpire asked Casey.

"That ball was right over the plate!" said Bolsun.

"Oh, you do, do you?" said the umpire to Casey.

"Yes, he does!" said Bolsun.

Bolsun and the umpire went on shouting. Each of them looked at Casey, and Casey looked at each of them. Casey's head kept going back and forth, but he didn't say anything. He couldn't get a word in edgewise.

"I'm the umpire," said the umpire, pushing back his little blue cap. "I calls 'em as I sees 'em. And I sees this ball as high and a little close. Now play ball!"

"Play ball nothing!" said Bolsun, pushing back his derby. "You called that one wrong and you know it! That's what Casey is telling you!"

By this time the umpire was red in the face. He leaned close to Casey and he poked him with his finger.

"I repeats," he said, "I'm the umpire."

"Casey knows you're the umpire," snapped Bolsun.

"I repeats," said the umpire, "I calls 'em as I sees 'em."

"How can you see 'em?" said Bolsun. "You're blind in one eye and wall-eyed in the other."

"And I repeats," said the umpire, "I sees this as a little high and a little close. Now are you going to play ball?"

"Not until you call that a strike," said Bolsun. "Casey's not playing ball till you call it a strike."

"No pitcher can talk that way to me!" shouted the umpire.

"You're being talked to that way right now," said Bolsun.

"Then get off the field!" roared the umpire at Casey. "Get off the field! Because I calls 'em as I sees 'em, and no pitcher can talk that way to me! Now get off the field, put in another pitcher, and let's PLAY BALL!"

25

"Look here, umpire—" Casey began.

"I've heard enough out of you!" bellowed the umpire. "One more word, and I'll give the game to the Wildcats!"

"Better do what he says, Casey," said Bolsun.

And while the rooters in the stands yelled and howled, Casey went back to the bench. Bolsun walked beside him, swinging his gold-handled cane so that it caught the shine of the sun.

"You shouldn't have done that, Casey," said Bolsun. "You shouldn't have talked that way to the umpire."

Bolsun put his derby on straight. He looked sadly at Casey, and shook his head. He walked out of the ball park, shaking his head as he went. Casey put in another pitcher, and the game went on.

Of course the other pitcher couldn't hold the Wildcats. They scored eight runs that inning, batting clear around the batting order. Casey sent in still another pitcher, but he didn't do much good either. The inning ended with the Wildcats leading fifteen to five.

Then Casey's team came up to bat. The Wildcats put them out so fast Casey hardly knew what was happening. The game was over, and his team had lost.

Casey left the ball park with Uncle Memphis and a crowd of Joneses.

"It's a sad day for the Joneses," they sighed.

"It is, and yet it isn't," said Casey. "Because I was tricked."

"What do you mean?" asked Uncle Memphis. "Didn't you talk back to the umpire?"

"Didn't say a word," said Casey. "Didn't get a chance to."

He told the Joneses what had happened, and they all agreed he'd been tricked.

"All the same, it's a sad day for the Joneses," said the Joneses. "A Jones has been out-smarted by a Brown."

"But not for long!" roared Uncle Memphis. "Casey, you come along with me. We're going to pay a little visit to Superintendent Bolsun Brown."

Casey and Uncle Memphis went to the depot. They went up to the top floor of the depot building, and into Bolsun Brown's office. Before they could see Bolsun, they had to see his junior clerk, his senior clerk, his secretary's secretary, and his secretary. But at last they saw Bolsun himself.

"Good afternoon, gentlemen," said Bolsun.

He was sitting in a swivel chair, with his feet up on his rolltop desk.

"Glad to see you," he said. "Glad you dropped around. If you hadn't called on me, I would have called on you. Because I'd like to remind you, Casey, of our little agreement. You said if you lost the ball game, you'd give up baseball. Yes, you said you'd give up baseball and stick to railroading.

Remember?"

"I remember," said Casey.

"And," said Bolsun, "you lost the ball game this afternoon. Remember?"

"And now you remember something," said Casey. "I didn't lose that ball game. I was tricked."

"Casey's right," put in Uncle Memphis. "You got him thrown out of the game. And he's not going to give up baseball."

Bolsun jumped to his feet.

"You mean to say you're not going to give up baseball?" he said, glaring at Casey.

"That's exactly what I mean," answered Casey.

"Casey," said Bolsun slowly, "I mean it for your own good. Baseball and railroading don't mix. If you go on playing ball, you'll lose your touch on the throttle."

"Maybe they don't mix for a Brown, but they mix for a

Jones!" shouted Casey. "Don't you tell me what's good for me! I was tricked, and I'm not going to quit playing ball."

"Then you'll never drive another locomotive for me!" shouted back Bolsun. "You'll never drive No. 638, No. 4, or any other hog on this line. From now on, Casey, you'll be the telegraph operator at the Oak Park station!"

"Me go back to pounding brass?" said Casey.

"Yes, you! And you'll be night operator, so you can play baseball all day! And when you get tired of pounding brass, maybe you'll give up baseball. And maybe then I'll let you go back to being an engineer."

"You can't do that to Casey Jones!" said Uncle Memphis.

"No, sir!" said Casey. "I quit!"

Bolsun sat down again in his swivel chair. He put his feet up on his rolltop desk, and he smiled.

"Oh, no," he said. "I'm not letting you go to another railroad. You're a good engineer, Casey. And if you stop playing baseball, you'll be one of the best. And I don't think you'll quit. Because if you do, I won't give you your clearance papers. And without your clearance papers you'll never get a job on any railroad. No, there won't be a Jones on any railroad at all. Good day, Mr. Memphis Jones. Good day, Casey.

Don't forget to report to work at the Oak Park station."

And that night Casey went back to pounding brass. He put away his high-bibbed overalls and his red thousand-mile shirt. He put away his black engineer's cap and his blue bandanna handkerchief. He wore a blue serge suit just like anybody else, with a white shirt and blue tie.

Of course Casey could pound brass with the best of them, and he kept the wires humming. Besides pounding the brass, he set the signal lights. If a train was to go ahead, he'd set the signal light on the green. If a train had to stop for orders, he'd set the signal light red. Then the engineer would stop his train and pick up his orders from Casey.

Night after night Casey sat all alone in the little station. It made him sad to listen to the long, lonesome wail of the locomotive whistles. It made him sad to listen to their engines moan. But he wouldn't give up playing baseball. He knew baseball would never make a Jones lose his touch on the throttle. And he knew he'd been tricked by Bolsun Brown.

One night Uncle Memphis came into the station, where Casey was pounding brass.

"Casey," said Uncle Memphis, "how long is this going to go on?"

Casey didn't know, and he said so.

"It's got to stop," said Uncle Memphis. "Do you know what's happening? The Browns are laughing at the Joneses. All over the city of Chicago, and way beyond. Bolsun is going around telling the Browns how he tricked you, and they're laughing their heads off."

"They can't do that," said Casey angrily. "Nobody has ever laughed at the Joneses before."

"They're doing it," said Uncle Memphis. "They're doing it. And there's only one thing left for you to do."

"What's that?" asked Casey.

32

"Bolsun tricked you, and you've got to trick him back," answered Uncle Memphis.

"But how, Uncle Memphis? How?"

"That's why I came here tonight," said Uncle Memphis. "You just leave everything to me."

"Go right ahead," said Casey. "When do you start."

"Right now," said Uncle Memphis.

The first thing Uncle Memphis did was to take the plugs out of the main trunk wires. After that he took the switch keys out of the telegraph stand. The telegraph stopped clacking, leaving the room quiet.

"That takes care of the telegraph," said Uncle Memphis.

The next thing he did was set the signal lights red, for both the east bound trains and the west bound trains.

"That takes care of the signal lights," he said.

Uncle Memphis told Casey to put on his hat and hand over the keys. Then they both stepped outside. Uncle Memphis locked the door of the station and said, "And that takes care of Bolsun Brown."

"I'm beginning to think it will," said Casey.

Outside the rails stretched east and west, shining in the light of the moon. Above the rails shone the red signal lights. Uncle Memphis looked around and pulled Casey into the bushes at the side of the tracks.

"We'll just wait here for a little while," he said. "Soon you'll see something worth seeing."

They didn't wait long before the west bound express came roaring up. When the engineer saw the red light, he pulled up in front of the station. He jumped down from the cab, went to the station, and rattled the door knob. The door wouldn't open, so he looked in the window. And what he saw made him take off his cap and scratch his head.

Then the conductor hopped off the train, together with a brakeman.

"Nobody here," Casey and Uncle Memphis heard the engineer say.

"There's got to be," said the conductor.

"See for yourself," said the engineer. "And we can't go on till we get the green light."

While the engineer was talking, the east bound limited pulled up at the station. The engineer jumped down from the cab and walked over to the other trainmen. And while they talked to him, the east bound local and the west bound freight pulled up. In no time at all there was a little crowd of trainmen standing in front of the station. Passengers looked out the windows of the cars, asking what was holding them up. The brakemen lit red lanterns, and the locomotives puffed steam.

"Guess you've seen enough to get the idea," said Uncle Memphis to Casey. "Now we'll go up to the Trainmen's Tavern."

The Trainmen's Tavern was on a little hill above the station. The back room was crowded with Joneses. Some of them were at the window, looking at the tie-up on the railroad. Others sat around the tables, which were loaded down with sandwiches, cider, and ale. When they saw Casey and Uncle Memphis they raised a cheer.

"It's a fine night for the Joneses," they said.

"But not for the Browns," said Uncle Memphis. "Especially not for Bolsun Brown." He picked up a glass of cider and sang:

> There's a red light on the track for
>   Bolsun Brown, Bolsun Brown,
> There's a red light on the track for
>   Bolsun Brown.
> There's a red light on the track,
> And it'll be there when he gets back,
> There's a red light on the track for
>   Bolsun Brown.

"Sure is," laughed Casey, pointing out the window.

Uncle Memphis and the other Joneses looked down. Below them trains were piled up as far as they could see. There were east bound trains and west bound trains. There were express trains, local trains, freight trains, and a few locomotives with just a tender and a caboose. Whistles were blowing and steam was hissing. In the glare of the headlights trainmen and passengers ran around. They shouted to each other and waved their arms. Every once in a while they'd point to the red signal lights, still shining above the tracks. It was the biggest tie-up in the history of railroads.

"Look at that smoke coming out of those smokestacks!" said the Joneses.

"That's a pretty sight," said Casey.

"Listen to those whistles blow!" said the Joneses.

"Sounds like music to me," said Casey.

The Joneses started to sing:

> The wind it blew up the railroad tracks,
>   It blew, It blew.
> The wind it blew up the railroad tracks,
> It blew way up and half way back,
> By Jiminy! How it blew!
>   By Jiminy! How it blew!

Uncle Memphis pulled out his gold stem-winding watch and said, "The news must have got to Bolsun by this time. Guess he'll soon be paying us a little visit."

It wasn't more than two minutes later that Bolsun burst into the room. He was puffing and out of breath. His derby was pushed over to one side of his head, and his stick-pin was stuck crooked in his tie.

"Casey," he puffed, "thought—puff, puff—I'd—puff, puff
—find you—puff, puff—here."

"Glad you did," said Casey. "Won't you step in and
join the fun?"

"That's right," said the Joneses. "Have a glass of cider,
Bolsun. Have a sandwich."

Bolsun's eyebrows came down over his eyes. His hand
shook on his gold-handled cane.

"What's the trouble?" asked Casey, as polite as you please.

"You know very well what's the trouble!" shouted Bolsun.
"You can hear those whistles blowing! You can hear that
steam hissing! You can see those trains piled up, waiting
for the green light to go ahead!"

Bolsun took a deep breath and roared, "Casey, give me

the keys to the station! I'm the Superintendent of this railroad, and I order you to give me those keys!"

Casey took a sip of cider.

"I'd like to obleege you, Bolsun," he said. "But first you'll have to answer a question or two."

"Such as?" asked Bolsun.

"Such as this," answered Casey. "Will you put me back on a locomotive?"

"No!" howled Bolsun.

"Then will you give me my clearance papers, so's I can get a job on another railroad?"

"No!" bellowed Bolsun.

"No keys," said Casey.

"May as well get back to our fun," said Uncle Memphis. He and the other Joneses started singing *There's a Red Light on the Track for Bolsun Brown*.

Bolsun was white in the face. Above the singing he could hear the whistles blowing and the steam hissing.

"All right," he said at last. "All right, Casey. I won't put you back on a locomotive. But I'll give you your clearance papers. You'll get them in the mail in the morning."

Uncle Memphis handed the keys to Bolsun, and Bolsun snatched them up.

"Well, Casey," said Bolsun. "You've got your clearance papers. But you'll never drive a locomotive again! Because I'll see that the story of what you did gets around! And no railroad will hire a man that started a tie-up! Then you'll come begging to me. But I'll never give you a job! And there won't be any Jones on the railroad at all!"

"Now, Bolsun," said Uncle Memphis. "You know you'll take Casey back. He's the only engineer who can handle No. 638."

"Ha!" laughed Bolsun. "The railroad can get along without a Jones. I'll handle No. 638 myself. Casey won't even get near her! If Casey ever sets foot in her cab, I'll quit my job as Superintendent! Then Casey can run the whole railroad! But he won't! And there will never be a Jones on the railroad again!"

With that he slammed the door and left. The Joneses looked at each other. Some of them began to say maybe it wasn't such a fine night for the Joneses after all. But Casey wasn't worried.

The next morning Casey got his clearance papers. Once again he put on his red thousand-mile shirt and his high-bibbed overalls. Once again he put his black engineer's cap on his head, and a blue bandanna around his neck for a sweat rag. He put a drop of oil on his handle-bar mustache to give it a gloss, and set off.

Casey went straight to the depot of the Illinois Central Railroad. He walked into the superintendent's office, showed his clearance papers, and asked for a job.

"Afraid not," was the superintendent's answer. "We know you're a good engineer. There's nothing wrong with your clearance papers. But we heard about that tie-up yesterday on the Central Pacific. We couldn't take a chance on a man who'd do something like that."

Casey saw that Bolsun had been right. There wasn't a railroad in the country that would give him a job. As he walked back to Mrs. Callahan's Rooming House for Railroad Men, he looked sad. His feet shuffled and his head hung low. But as soon as he was in the front parlor with Uncle Memphis, he began to smile.

"What's there to smile about?" asked Uncle Memphis after Casey had told him what happened. "Have you seen this?"

He shoved a newspaper into Casey's hand. On the second page was a big notice:

TWO WEEKS FROM TONIGHT

First run of the Cannon Ball Express
from Chicago to San Francisco
with

LOCOMOTIVE NO. 638

Leaves the Chicago Depot at 8: 52

The Cannon Ball will have the
right of way and will attempt
to break all speed records

ENGINEER—SUPERINTENDENT BOLSUN BROWN

"Bolsun can't handle No. 638," said Uncle Memphis.

"And he's not going to," said Casey. "Because I'm going to be in the cab of that locomotive."

"What's your plan?" asked Uncle Memphis.

"Never mind that now," said Casey. "You go around looking sad. You tell all the other Joneses to look sad. But on the night No. 638 makes her run, you and the other Joneses buy yourselves a round-trip ticket to 'Frisco. You get on board the Cannon Ball, and you'll see some real railroading."

Uncle Memphis wasn't so sure. Still, he did what Casey told him. He went around looking sad. He kept saying, "Never thought I'd see the day when there wasn't a Jones on the railroad." And all the other Joneses looked so sad even the Browns felt sorry for them.

Casey looked sadder than any of them. On the day No. 638 was to make her run, he dropped in at the Blue Front Restaurant. Bolsun Brown was sitting at the counter. Casey sat down himself, giving a little moan.

"What'll it be, Casey," asked the counterman. "You name it—I've got it."

43

"I'm not hungry," said Casey. "I'll just have a Trainmen's Delight."

"Trainmen's Delight," repeated the counterman. He gave Casey a T-bone steak, with French fried potatoes and cream gravy.

"Lost your appetite?" asked Bolsun.

"Kind of," said Casey.

"Sorry to hear it," said Bolsun. "How come you're not out playing baseball on a nice day like this."

"Can't get my heart in it," said Casey.

"Too bad," said Bolsun. "Too bad when a man can't play ball or railroad."

Casey sighed.

"Bolsun," he said, "if I bought a ticket could I ride on the Cannon Ball tonight?"

Bolsun threw back his head and laughed.

"Oh, no, Casey," he said: "You're not even going to get near No. 638. Memphis can ride, and any other Jones, if they want to. But not you, Casey. Can't take chances. I'm going to have guards all around. You'll have to read about it in the paper."

"That's what I thought," said Casey slowly.

He finished his Trainmen's Delight, then went back to the rooming house. He stayed there until it was night, and when he came out again nobody would have known it was Casey.

Because Casey had shaved off his mustache. His face was covered with soot and coal dust. He was wearing somebody else's overalls, and somebody else's thousand-mile shirt. He had an old banged-up oil can in his pocket and he didn't have any watch at all.

Casey made his way to the depot, where No. 638 was

getting up steam. She was still decked out in flags and red-white-and-blue bunting. She was clean and shining and ready to go. A few hostlers were still working over her, wiping off a few specks of dust.

Casey pushed his way through the crowd and saw the bright new cars behind No. 638. People were getting on, waving good-by. Among them was Uncle Memphis and the Joneses. A guard at the door of each car watched them, to make sure Casey wasn't trying to sneak on.

Then Casey saw Bolsun Brown. He wasn't wearing his derby, and he wasn't carrying his gold-handled cane. He had on brand new engineer's clothes, and he carried his orders in his hand. After Bolsun started talking to the conductor, Casey hurried to the locomotive. There was a whole ring of guards around No. 638, but they let Casey through.

Casey climbed up to the cab. He poked the fireman with his finger and said, "Seems there's been a mistake."

"What kind of mistake?" asked the fireman. His face was covered with soot and coal dust, just like Casey's.

"Seems you weren't supposed to be the fireman on this run," said Casey. "Seems that I was."

"But I got my call from the call boy!" said the fireman.

"He's the one who made the mistake," said Casey. "Got everything all twisted up. Bolsun Brown just found out and told me I was to be the fireman on this hog."

"Guess I'd better go, then," said the fireman.

"That's right," said Casey. "And don't let Bolsun see you. He's angry enough as it is."

The fireman climbed down, and Casey picked up his shovel. He was shoveling away when Bolsun mounted to the cab. Casey kept his face turned away from Bolsun and kept on shoveling coal.

"Looks bad," said Bolsun in a squeaky voice. "There are

storms all along the way. There are washouts and landslides. Looks bad."

"I'm not worried," said Casey. "Can't anything stop a Brown."

Casey went on shoveling coal till he heard the conductor yell, "Board! All a-boar-r-rd!"

"There's the brakeman giving us the highball," said Bolsun. "Jingle the brass, fireman."

Casey pulled the cord of the bell. Bolsun opened the throttle, and No. 638 began to pull out.

"Chug-chug-chug!" went her engine. Then it went *Ssssssssssst!* and stopped.

Bolsun's hand was shaking on the throttle.

"Maybe I've lost my touch," he said.

"How come?" asked Casey. "Have you been playing baseball?"

"Why, no," said Bolsun. "What makes you say that?"

"Always heard baseball made an engineer lose his touch," answered Casey.

Bolsun wiped his face with his sweat rag and tried again. This time No. 638 roared out of the depot. The only trouble was, she didn't run smooth. She rattled and wheezed and swung from side to side. She didn't run fast at all. When Bolsun tried to blow her whistle, all he got was a little peep.

"Well, we're on our way," said Bolsun, trying to smile.

"Sure are," said Casey, trying *not* to smile.

It wasn't long before they ran into the storm. The rain poured down. The thunder made a noise louder than No. 638. Every once in a while lightning flashed down, striking a tree or pole along the tracks.

Suddenly Bolsun let out a yell and stopped the train.

"Look!" he said.

Right below them was a deep valley. There was a trestle bridge over the valley, but it had been struck by lightning. Now it was burning, and soon there wouldn't be any bridge at all.

"Can't cross through that fire," said Bolsun. "And we can't cross without any bridge. I guess we'd better turn back. We'll never get to 'Frisco tonight."

The conductor and a brakeman ran up to the locomotive to see what was stopping them. They saw the trestle bridge burning, and they said the same thing as Bolsun.

"Casey Jones could get her through," said Casey quietly.

"Don't think he could," said the conductor. "And he's not anywhere near No. 638."

"Look here, fireman," said Bolsun, "I've heard enough talk about Casey Jones."

"And you're going to hear a lot more!" shouted Casey, wiping the soot and coal dust off his face with his sweat rag. He stepped close to Bolsun and opened the fire door. The engine fire lit up his face so that Bolsun could see it.

"You couldn't be!" said Bolsun. "You can't . . . ! You're not . . . ! But you are Casey Jones!"

"Casey Jones it is," said Casey. "Don't have my handle-bar mustache, but the rest of me is here. Bolsun, do you remember what you said the night of the tie-up? Remember how you said if I set foot in the cab of No. 638 I could have your job?"

Bolsun sank back into the fireman's seat.

"You win, Casey," he said. "I don't know how you did it, but you're here. I remember what I said and I won't go back on my word. You're the new Superintendent of the Central Pacific Railroad." Then he jumped up and shouted,

"But if you think you can get this train to 'Frisco you're crazy!"

"That's no way to talk to the Superintendent of this railroad," said Casey. He ordered the conductor and the brakeman to board the train. A cheer came from the Joneses when they heard the news.

Casey sat down on the engineer's seat and put his hand on the throttle. He pulled the whistle cord, and blew his whippoorwill call on the whistle. Then he put the engine into reverse, and the train started rolling backward.

"Ha!" said Bolsun. "I knew it! I knew it! You're taking her back!"

"Just hold on there, Bolsun," said Casey. "You'll see what I'm going to do."

Casey did take the train back to the depot at Chicago. But that wasn't the end of the trip. He picked up a fireman, and asked the passengers if they wanted to go along to 'Frisco.

"I'm going!" said Uncle Memphis. "If Casey says we'll get there, we will!"

"We may get to 'Frisco but we'll all be dead!" howled Bolsun. "There's a bridge out."

"Casey will get us there, bridge or no bridge," said the Joneses.

Most of the passengers boarded the train again.

"Coming along, Bolsun?" asked Casey.

"I'm a fool to do it," answered Bolsun, "but I will. The Browns are just as brave as the Joneses."

Casey told Bolsun to ride with him in the cab. Then he told the fireman to jingle the brass. He blew a blast on the whistle, opened the throttle, and pulled out. And No. 638 went rolling along, rolling along. Her piston rods shot in and out. She left a long line of smoke against the sky, and she made a noise like thunder.

"Watch those drivers roll!" said Casey. "Watch her steam gauge rise!"

"We'll never get to 'Frisco," said Bolsun. "And if we do, we'll all be dead."

"Build up that fire, tar pot," said Casey to the fireman.

53

"I'm building her," said the fireman. "I'm putting black on white."

"Go to it, diamond pusher!" said Casey. "I'm going to get to 'Frisco, but I'll need steam!"

No. 638 went highballing along with a terrible roar. Her flags and bunting streamed in the wind. Faster and faster she went, until they got to the valley.

"The bridge is out!" shrieked Bolsun. "It's our last ride!"

Casey glanced at the steam gauge and the water gauge. He opened her throttle wide. No. 638 rushed ahead—and

her speed was so fast she cleared the valley. She flew from
one side to the other, and came down with a little bump.

"That's railroading!" said the fireman.

"I can't believe it!" said Bolsun. "I saw it, but I can't
believe it!"

After that, of course, Casey didn't have a bit of trouble.
He kept No. 638 going, stopping only to pick up coal or
water or a fresh fireman. No. 638 passed state after state. She
raced up the Rocky Mountains and down again. She crossed
plains and valleys and mountains, and by morning she was

in 'Frisco. She'd broken every record ever made.

Casey pulled into the depot, where a crowd of people waited to give him a cheer. Uncle Memphis and the Joneses jumped from the train, laughing and shouting.

"It's a great day for the Joneses!" they said.

"But a bad day for the Browns," said Bolsun. He turned to Casey and said, "Well, Casey, you got her to 'Frisco. You're a great engineer, and now you're Superintendent of the railroad. I hope you like your new job. Good-by, Casey."

"Hold on there, Bolsun," said Casey. "I was meant to be an engineer. You were meant to be a Superintendent. You keep running the railroad, and I'll keep running locomotives.

Only don't tell me to stop playing baseball. This railroad needs Browns *and* Joneses to run her right."

"Casey," said Bolsun, "do you mean that?"

Casey nodded his head.

"Then as Superintendent of this railroad," said Bolsun, "I order you to get out there and pitch your razzle-dazzle ball! Because you're a Jones, and nothing can hurt your touch on the throttle."

Casey pitched his razzle-dazzle ball. After that Bolsun, Casey, Uncle Memphis and the Joneses went to the Blue Goose Restaurant. They had Trainmen's Delights all around, with speeches and a general good time.

And ever since then, there have been both Joneses and Browns on the railroad.

HOW OLD STORMALONG CAPTURED MOCHA DICK

STORY BY

IRWIN SHAPIRO

PICTURES BY

DONALD McKAY

THERE are many stories about who captured Mocha Dick, the Great White Whale, or Moby Dick, as he was sometimes called. But any sailorman worth his salt knows that it was Old Stormalong—and he had to become a cowboy to do it.

Alfred Bulltop Stormalong was the greatest sailor who ever lived. He stood four fathoms tall in his stocking feet. His eyes were as blue as a calm sea. His hair was as black as a storm cloud. He could whistle shrill like the wind in the rigging; he could hoot like a foghorn; and he could talk ordinary, just like anyone else. Stormalong had one fault. He was always complaining that they didn't make ships big enough for him.

One windy night Stormalong was sitting in the Sailors'

Snug Haven, the inn that served the best shark soup in the
town of Nantucket. He was sitting cross-legged on the floor
so that his head wouldn't bump the ceiling. He ate six dozen
oysters, then called for some shark soup, which he drank
from a dory. Beside him sat Captain Joshua Skinner of the
good ship *Dolphin*, and some members of the crew. Stormalong was to sail with them the next morning to catch whales
in the Pacific Ocean.

"Captain Skinner," said Stormalong, "on this voyage I'm
going to capture Mocha Dick."

"Hm," said Captain Skinner. "You've said that five times
before. And five times the white whale escaped you."

"This time he won't escape!" shouted Stormalong, hooting
like a foghorn. Then he added in an ordinary voice, "And I

mean it, too."

"Hm," said Captain Skinner. "You meant it the other five times. And still Mocha Dick swims the seas."

"Aye, 'tis easy to capture the white whale—with words," said a little sailor with red whiskers, while all the other sailors laughed.

"Laugh while you may," said Stormalong angrily. "You'll be singing a different tune when the *Dolphin* comes back to port."

"If you are so sure of yourself," said the innkeeper, "write it down here." And he handed Stormalong one of the slates on which he kept accounts.

"Aye, that I will," said Stormalong. Picking up the slate, he wrote in big letters:

On this voyage of the Dolphin I will capture Mocha Dick.

Signed, Alfred Bulltop Stormalong

The innkeeper hung the slate up over the fireplace for all to see.

"Aye, mateys!" roared Stormalong. "This time Mocha Dick will meet his doom!"

Stormalong finished his shark soup in one gulp. Then he whistled shrill like the wind in the rigging, and left the inn.

The next morning a crowd of people was at the dock to say good-by to the *Dolphin's* brave crew.

"Good luck, lads!" they shouted. "A short voyage and a greasy one! Fair winds, calm seas! Beware of Mocha Dick!"

"Let Mocha Dick beware, for Alfred Bulltop Stormalong is out to capture him!" said Stormalong, hooting like a fog-horn.

"Belay there! Enough of your boasting!" said Captain Skinner. Then he turned to the first mate and said, "Cast off!"

And a cheer went up as the *Dolphin* caught the wind in her sails and went out to the open sea.

For nine months the *Dolphin* sailed the Pacific Ocean. Wherever she went, there was always a lookout in the crow's nest high on the mast. Every time the lookout spied a whale, he would shout, "Blo-o-ows! Thar she blows!" And the men would jump into rowboats and give chase to the whale.

One day the lookout in the crow's nest called out,

"*Blo-o-ows!* Thar she blows! Whale off the port side! Thar she blows and breaches! And Mocha Dick, at that!"

"Man the boats!" ordered the captain. "Lower away!"

The men set out over the side of the ship in little boats and rowed toward Mocha Dick. Stormalong stood in the stern of his boat, waving his harpoon in the air.

"After him, me hearties!" he shouted. "Faster, lads, faster! There he is now!"

And indeed they could see Mocha Dick's ugly face rising out of the sea. With a rumble and a roar the Great White Whale sent a spout of water high into the air. He was almost as big as the *Dolphin*, and he was the color of sea-foam in the light of a misty moon. As if to warn Stormalong, he opened his mouth and showed his great sharp teeth.

"After him, mateys!" cried Stormalong. "A dead whale or
a stove boat!"

With a shout, Stormalong let his harpoon fly at Mocha
Dick. It stuck in the whale's back. But Mocha Dick just
gave himself a shake and began to swim away. The harpoon
was attached to the boat by a long rope, and as Mocha Dick
swam along he pulled the boat after him.

"Hold fast, mates!" said Stormalong. "Here we go on a
sleigh ride!"

Swoosh! And off they went across the water. Faster and
faster swam Mocha Dick, with the little boat bobbing and
bouncing after him. Soon they had left the *Dolphin* far
behind.

Suddenly Mocha Dick stopped. He heaved himself into

the air, and the rope broke with a snap. The harpoon remained in his back, a little bit of rope flying from it like a
flag of victory. He dove below the water, gave a flip of his
tail, and the boat overturned. With a splash, Stormalong and
his mates tumbled into the sea.

"We are lost!" cried one of the sailors. "Mocha Dick is
coming back! He will swallow us all!"

But Mocha Dick just pushed his way close to Stormalong
and opened his mouth in a big grin. His body shook as
though he were laughing. Then he spouted a stream of water
right into Stormalong's face, grinned again, and swam away.

"By my boots and breeches!" burst out a little sailor with
a lot of red whiskers. "Mocha Dick laughed at Stormalong, and laughed at Stormalong, and spit in his eye!"

All the sailors began to laugh so hard that they almost went to the bottom of the sea. They laughed until their sides ached, and then they laughed some more. They were still laughing when the *Dolphin* caught up with them

"What's so funny?" asked Captain Skinner after the men had climbed on board.

"Mocha Dick laughed at Stormalong and spit in his eye!" said the little sailor with red whiskers.

Captain Skinner began to laugh so hard that the first mate had to grab him by the seat of his pants to keep him from falling overboard. Then the second mate had to grab the first mate to keep *him* from falling overboard.

"And Stormalong the man who boasted that he would capture Mocha Dick!" sputtered the captain. "Ho, ho! Ha, ha!"

"Ho, ho! Ha, ha! Har, har!" laughed the sailors. "Ho, har!"
The little sailor with red whiskers began to sing:

"Stormalong said he'd get Mocha Dick,
    Aye, mates, 'tis no lie,
But the Great White Whale just laughed in his face,
    And spit right in his eye.
To my aye, aye, right in Stormalong's eye,
To my aye, aye, Mister Stormalong's eye."

Stormalong felt so ashamed that he went below and didn't
come up on deck for a week.

For three more months the *Dolphin* sailed the Pacific.
Stormalong did his share of the work, but he never hooted like

a foghorn or whistled shrill like the wind in the rigging. He hardly said a word.

When the *Dolphin* slid into the harbor at Nantucket, the sailors told everyone what had happened. Soon all Nantucket knew that Mocha Dick had laughed at Stormalong and spit in his eye. Poor Stormalong ran away to the beach where he could be alone.

All day long he sat on the beach, sighing and sighing. He sighed so hard that the sea became choppy. At last Stormalong picked himself up and walked to the Sailors' Snug Haven.

The first thing he saw when he entered the inn was the slate hanging over the fireplace. And on it were the words:

On this voyage of the Dolphin I will capture
Mocha Dick.

       Signed, Alfred Bulltop Stormalong

Below these words someone had written:

**But the Great White Whale just laughed at him
and spit in his eye.**

Stormalong sat down and ordered some shark soup, which
he drank from a dory. He topped it off with a keg of New
England rum, then went over to Captain Skinner and said,
"Captain, I've made my last voyage."

"Surely not, laddie," said Captain Skinner kindly. "Oh, no!"

"Aye, Captain," said Stormalong. "I'll never go to sea again. I'm going to be a farmer."

"A farmer!" said Captain Skinner. "You'll never be a farmer, my lad. You've got salt water in your veins. Wherever you go, you'll hear the sea calling to you."

"No," said Stormalong. "They don't build ships big enough for me. I can't get the kinks out of my muscles. And if I can't get the kinks out of my muscles, I can't capture Mocha Dick. And if I can't capture Mocha Dick, I'm no whaler. And if I'm no whaler, I'm no sailor. And if I'm no sailor, the sea is no place for me. I'm going off to be a farmer."

"Well, lad," said Captain Skinner, "if you must go, you must. Good luck to you, and may you reach a safe harbor. But you'll be coming back to sea some day. And when you

do, old Captain Joshua Skinner will give you a berth."

"Thank you, Captain," said Stormalong. "Good-by, Captain."

The next morning Stormalong left Nantucket for the mainland. His dufflebag over his shoulder, he walked down the road. In the light of the morning sun his shadow stretched before him, three counties long.

Stormalong rambled about the Hudson Valley, then stepped over the Allegheny Mountains and ambled about the Shenandoah Valley. He took a little side trip to the Cumberland Mountains, and spent a day in the Tennessee Valley. He walked along the Ohio River, then over the rolling hills of Indiana and the prairies of Illinois. But not until he crossed the Mississippi River to Missouri did he find what he was

73

looking for.

"Aye," said Stormalong, "this is a country where a full-sized man can get the kinks out of his muscles."

He was in a great forest, where men with axes were chopping down trees. Clong! Clong! went the axes, and the trees crashed to the ground.

"Are you farmers, mateys?" asked Stormalong in his foghorn voice. All the men stopped their work to look at him.

"I reckon we are," said one of the men.

"That's good," said Stormalong. "I'm new to farming, and I'll thank you to tell me what to do."

"Right now we're clearing away the forest so's we can grow our crops," was the answer.

Stormalong borrowed the biggest ax they had, then said,

"Now, mates, just sit down in the shade and rest a while. I mean to do some plain and fancy chopping, to get the kinks out of my muscles."

Stormalong rolled up his sleeves and went to work. By nightfall he had cleared enough land for a hundred farms.

"Who are you?" asked the astonished farmers.

"Alfred Bulltop Stormalong is the name, mateys," said Stormalong. "They don't make ships big enough for me, so I can't get the kinks out of my muscles. If I can't get the kinks out of my muscles, I can't capture Mocha Dick. And if I can't capture Mocha Dick, I'm no whaler. And if I'm no whaler, then I'm no sailor. And if I'm no sailor, my place is on shore. So I came out here to be a farmer, and I'll thank you to tell me just what to do, and how to do it."

75

And he hooted like a foghorn and whistled shrill like the wind in the rigging.

"The next thing is to clear out the stumps and stones and start planting," said the farmers. "But first you'd better build yourself a cabin to live in."

"A cabin it is, me hearties," said Stormalong. By the time the moon came out he had built himself a cabin.

The next morning Stormalong got up before the sun and started to plow. He didn't use a horse. He just pushed the plow along himself, while stones and stumps flew in all directions.

"Where's your horse?" asked the farmers, more astonished than ever. "We never heard tell of plowing without a horse, a mule, or at least a team of oxen." They shook their heads.

"Didn't know you were supposed to have one," said Stormalong. "But no harm done. If you'll just toss these rocks and
stumps into a pile, I'll finish this little job of work."

By the time it was evening, Stormalong had plowed enough
land for a hundred farms.

"What's next, me hearties?" he asked. "For I've got the
kinks out of my muscles and I'm rarin' to go."

"Plant the seed," said the farmers.

When the farmers got up the next morning, they found
Stormalong stretched out under a tree.

"Glad you're up," he said. "I've planted all the seed. Nothing to it. What do I do now?"

"Just wait for the crops to start growing," said the farmers.
"Unless you have some cows or chickens or pigs to look

after."

"I can't look after cows or chickens or pigs," said Stormalong. "I'm too big for 'em. But I don't like this idea of waiting. I'll get kinks in my muscles."

It was hard for Stormalong to sit around doing nothing. At night he could hear the wind blowing through the trees of the forest. The leaves went hiss, swish, like the sound of the sea. The branches creaked like the rigging of a ship. Stormalong dreamt that he was a sailor again.

In the daytime Stormalong would climb the tallest tree in the forest. He would gaze out over the rolling hills, which looked like the waves of the sea. The tree swayed in the wind, and Stormalong imagined he was in the crow's nest of the *Dolphin*, keeping a sharp lookout for whale the while.

A big cloud floated past in the sky. To Stormalong it looked like Mocha Dick.

"*Blo-o-ows!*" he shouted. "Thar she blows! Whale off the starboard side! Thar she blows and breaches! And Mocha Dick, at that! After him, me hearties! A dead whale or a stove boat!"

Then one day a storm came up. The sky was as black as the bottom of a well. Lightning flashed, thunder roared, while the wind went howling through the forest like a madman.

"Hooray, a storm!" shouted Stormalong to the farmers. "Now I can get the kinks out of my muscles. Avast there, mateys! Storm ahead! All hands on deck!"

All of a sudden one of the farmers stuck his head out of the window of his cabin, and looked at Stormalong.

"What's all the fuss?" he asked.

"Storm!" said Stormalong. "Pipe all hands on deck! What do farmers do in a storm, matey?"

"Let 'er storm," said the farmer. "Nothing else to do."

Stormalong was so surprised he couldn't say anything. He just stood there, the lightning flashing around his head, the rain dripping down his shoulders.

"I've had enough of this," he said at last. "I can't sit around and do nothing when there's a storm. I guess I just wasn't cut out to be a farmer."

He went to his cabin, threw his dufflebag over his shoulder, then waved good-by to the farmers.

"So long," he said. "I'm going west to be a cowboy."

Stormalong rambled about the dusty plains of Texas, then

ambled over to Oklahoma. He took a side trip to the Rocky
Mountains, and followed the Sweetwater River into Wy-
oming. He walked across the salt flats of Utah and the
plateau of Arizona, but not until he came to New Mexico
did he find what he was looking for.

"Aye," he said, "this is a country where a full-sized man
can get the kinks out of his muscles."

Stormalong went into a store to buy himself a cowboy
outfit.

"Matey," he said to the storekeeper, "I want a ten-gallon
hat, chaps, a checkered shirt, Spanish boots with pointed
toes, silver spurs, and a pretty bandana."

The storekeeper looked Stormalong up and down.

"Stranger," he said, "you're the biggest galoot that ever

blew into this man's town. I can sell you what you want, but it will have to be made special."

It took eight weeks to make Stormalong's cowboy outfit While he was waiting, Stormalong learned how to use a lariat. With his lariat Stormalong lassoed the wild mustang that roamed the plains. The mustang was a little too small for Stormalong, but it was the biggest horse he could get.

Then Stormalong got a job as a cowboy on the Triple Star Ranch.

"Mateys," he said, "I've never been a cowboy before, and I'll thank you to tell me what to do."

"It's round-up time, pardner," said the cowboys. "First thing to do is round up the steers."

"Just sit down and rest yourself, me hearties," said Storm-

along. "I'll round 'em up, just to get the kinks out of my muscles."

When evening came, Stormalong had rounded up all the steers.

"Who are you?" asked the astonished cowboys.

"Alfred Bulltop Stormalong is the name," answered Stormalong. "They don't make ships big enough for me, so I can't get the kinks out of my muscles. If I can't get the kinks out of my muscles, I can't capture Mocha Dick. And if I can't capture Mocha Dick, I'm no whaler. And if I'm no whaler, then I'm no sailor. And if I'm no sailor, my place is on shore. I tried to be a farmer, but I couldn't. So I came out here to be a cowboy, and I'll thank you to tell me what to do."

"The next thing to do is brand the steers," said the cow-

boys.

Stormalong got up before the sun the next morning and started to brand the steers. By the time the cowboys got up all the steers had been branded.

"What's next, me hearties?" asked Stormalong. "For I've got the kinks out of my muscles and I'm rarin' to go."

"Just ride around and keep an eye on the steers. We call it riding herd," said the cowboys.

Stormalong rode herd with the other cowboys. At night they sat around the campfire, playing the guitar and singing songs. Stormalong had a guitar made special, and when he played it the mountains would echo for miles around.

Stormalong soon began to get tired of being a cowboy. There wasn't enough to do, and he was getting kinks in his

muscles. At night he would wake up and look around. In the
moonlight the plain stretched out like a calm sea, while the
mountains stood up like islands.

"Avast, mateys!" shouted Stormalong. "We're becalmed!
More sail, more sail! Break out more sail, me hearties, for we
must capture Mocha Dick, the Great White Whale!"

One day a huge black cloud filled the sky and the rain
began to come down. Lightning flashed, thunder boomed,
and the wind raced across the plain like wild horses.

Stormalong waved his ten-gallon hat in the air and shouted,
"All hands on deck! Storm blowing up! All hands on deck!"
And he hooted like a foghorn and whistled shrill like the
wind in the rigging.

"What's the rumpus, pardner?" asked one of the cowboys.

"Storm!" said Stormalong. "What do cowboys do in a storm, matey? She's a-rippin' and a-snortin'."

"Let 'er rip and snort," said the cowboy. "Nothing else to do about it."

Stormalong sat down on a big rock. The wind howled around him, and the water dripped off his hat like a waterfall.

"I just can't sit around and do nothing when there's a storm," he said. "I guess I'm no more a cowboy than I was a farmer."

Stormalong seemed to hear the voice of Captain Skinner saying, "Aye, lad, you'll never be able to give up the sea. You've got salt water in your veins. Wherever you go, you'll hear the sea calling to you."

"You were right, Captain Skinner!" shouted Stormalong.

"Maybe the ships are too small for a full-sized man. Maybe I'll get kinks in my muscles and won't be able to capture Mocha Dick. Maybe I'm no whaler, and maybe I'm no sailor. But I'll go back to sea if I have to be a cabin boy, for I'll never be happy anywhere else."

Stormalong turned his mustang loose on the plains. He threw his dufflebag over one shoulder, and slung his guitar over the other.

"So long, mateys," he said to the cowboys. Then he started walking east, toward Nantucket and the sea.

It was a wet, misty morning when Stormalong got to Nantucket. For a long time he stood on a hill, sniffing in the salt sea air. He could see the harbor, with masts of ships sticking up into the sky. When he caught sight of the waves breaking

on the shore, he hooted like a foghorn and whistled shrill like the wind in the rigging.

"The sea is the place for me," he said. "And now for the Sailors' Snug Haven and some of that good shark soup."

When Stormalong got to the Sailors' Snug Haven he wiped the mist from his eyes and looked around. Everything was the same as it had been. Over the fireplace hung the slate with these words on it:

On this voyage of the Dolphin I will capture Mocha Dick.

Signed, Alfred Bulltop Stormalong

But the Great White Whale just laughed at him and spit in his eye.

"A cowboy in Nantucket!" said a voice behind him. "You're a long way from home, matey."

Stormalong turned around. There sat Captain Skinner.

"The sea is my home, Captain," said Stormalong, hooting like a foghorn and whistling shrill like the wind in the rigging.

"By my boots and breeches!" said the captain. "It's Stormalong, for there's no one else who can hoot like a foghorn and whistle shrill like the wind in the rigging."

"Aye," said Stormalong, "Alfred Bulltop Stormalong it is, and I'll never leave the sea again."

"I knew you'd be back, lad," said Captain Skinner. "Now sit down beside me and tell me your adventures."

Stormalong ordered some shark soup, which he drank from a dory. He told Captain Skinner all his adventures, and when

he had finished he said, "And now, Captain, will you give me my old berth on the *Dolphin?*"

"Aye, laddie. But you used to complain that the *Dolphin* was too small for you. Well, she's still the same size, but you're bigger than ever."

"She'll be big enough for me," said Stormalong. "I'll go to sea in a washtub if I can't get anything else."

"Spoken like a true seaman!" laughed Captain Skinner. "Well, I must leave you now, for I've some business to do. We sail at six tomorrow morning. Be sure that you're on time."

When Captain Skinner stood up Stormalong saw that one of his legs was gone. In its place was a wooden peg-leg.

"Your leg, Captain!" said Stormalong. "What happened?"

"It was bit off by Mocha Dick on my last voyage. The

white whale bit off my leg and sent two of my crew to the bottom of the sea."

"Captain Skinner," cried Stormalong, "I won't rest until I've captured Mocha Dick."

"No, lad," said the captain. "Never again will I battle Mocha Dick. He's more fearful than ever. I'll lose no more of my men to the monster." And with that he left the inn.

When Stormalong came on board the *Dolphin* the next morning, the crew began to laugh. He was still wearing his cowboy outfit, and he was so bowlegged from riding the mustang that a ship could have sailed between his legs.

"Avast there, Stormalong!" said Captain Skinner. "Get below and put on some proper duds. Stormalong or no Stormalong, I'll have no cowboys on my ship."

"Captain, I'd like to do as you say, but this cowboy outfit

91

was made special, and I'm going to keep on wearing it."

Captain Skinner grew red in the face.

"I'm captain of this ship, and you'll obey my orders!" he roared.

"Captain," said Stormalong, "I know you're the captain. But captain or no captain, I'm going to wear my cowboy outfit."

Stormalong began to hop up and down, so that the *Dolphin* rocked in the water.

"Belay there, Stormalong!" shouted the sailors. "Sit down, you're rocking the boat!"

"Stop, Stormalong! You'll sink the ship!" cried the captain.

Stormalong kept hopping up and down.

"I won't stop until you say it's all right for me to wear my cowboy outfit," he said. "And you can lay to that!"

92

"Wear what you like, you stubborn walrus!" said the captain, and Stormalong stopped hopping up and down.

A crowd had gathered on shore to say good-by to Captain Skinner and his crew.

"Good luck!" they called. "A short voyage and a greasy one!"

Captain Skinner was so angry that he didn't want to say good-by to anyone.

"Cast off!" he bellowed.

The *Dolphin* was raring to go. She took the wind in her sails and made for the open sea.

It was not long before the lookout in the crow's nest sang out, "*Blo-o-ows! Thar she blows!* Whale off the port side!"

"Yipee!" shouted Stormalong, like a cowboy. Still dressed in his cowboy outfit, he jumped into his boat. It made Cap-

tain Skinner angry to see a cowboy in a whaling boat. But he didn't say anything. He was afraid Stormalong would start hopping up and down again.

Stormalong soon showed that he could still catch whales.

"By the Great Horn Spoon," said Captain Skinner to himself, "Stormalong is a real sailorman, even if he does dress like a cowboy."

Then one day the lookout in the crow's nest shouted, "*Blo-o-ows!* Thar she blows and breaches! And Mocha Dick, at that! It's the Great White Whale, mates!"

"All hands aloft!" ordered Captain Skinner. "Break out more sail. We're going to get away from these waters as fast as we can. I'll not battle Mocha Dick again."

"Captain," said Stormalong, "are you really going to let it be said that a Nantucket whaler ran away from a whale?"

"Mocha Dick is no ordinary whale. He is a monster, and I'll lose no more of my men to him," said Captain Skinner.

"Let me go after him," begged Stormalong. "He'll not laugh at me this time."

"Stow your chatter and help loose the sails," Captain Skinner bellowed. "I'm the captain of the *Dolphin*, Mr. Stormalong, and I forbid you to go after Mocha Dick. Now get aloft before I have you put in irons!"

But just then the lookout in the crow's nest gave a terrible cry.

"Mocha Dick is coming after us! He's going to bump the ship!"

Captain Skinner ran to the rail. There was Mocha Dick, roaring and snorting and plunging. He rushed straight at the *Dolphin*, and *bump!* the stern of the ship rose into the air.

"We are lost!" cried the sailors. "Mocha Dick will sink the ship. We are lost!"

"Not yet, mateys!" said Stormalong.

And leaping over the rail, he landed smack on Mocha Dick's back.

"Yipee!" shouted Stormalong, and he began to ride Mocha Dick like a cowboy riding a bucking broncho. He hung on with one hand and waved his ten-gallon hat with the other.

Mocha Dick thrashed about, trying to throw Stormalong off his back. Stormalong only laughed and waved his hat again.

"Ride him, cowboy!" cheered the sailors. "Ride him, Stormalong!"

Snorting with rage, the white whale leaped into the air. Then he dove deep under the water, trying to drown Storm-

along. But Stormalong took a deep breath and held his nose. Mocha Dick heaved himself into the air again. He tossed and twisted and turned. Then he began to swim furiously about. He went zig-zagging across the ocean so fast that the zigs and the zags became all mixed up. Captain Skinner and his crew grew dizzy watching them.

"Ride him, cowboy!" they yelled. "Ride him, Stormalong!"

"Yipee! *Wahoo!*" shouted Stormalong, hooting like a fog-horn and whistling shrill like the wind in the rigging.

For three days Stormalong rode Mocha Dick. Once when he passed close to the ship he called out, "I'm getting hungry, mates. How about some coffee and a sandwich?"

The cook made him a washtub full of coffee and a sandwich three yards long. When Stormalong passed by again, a sailor stood on the jib boom and handed them to Storm-

along.

On the third day Mocha Dick's strength was almost gone. But he made one great try to throw Stormalong off his back. He dove deep under the water. He turned somersaults. He tossed and twisted and rolled from side to side. He went around in circles, like a dog chasing his tail. Around and around he went, until the water foamed like milk. He leaped high into the air and came down with a tremendous splash. Then a shudder ran through his body and he was still.

"Hooray!" shouted the sailors. "Hooray for Stormalong!"

"This is the end of the Great White Whale," said a big sailor with a crooked nose. "He just wore himself out."

"No," said a little sailor with red whiskers, "he died of a broken heart."

"Hooray!" shouted the sailors again and again. "Hooray

for Stormalong!"

"Aye, lads, you may well cheer," said Captain Skinner. "Stormalong has done a great thing. No more will Mocha Dick send honest seamen to their death."

Then the *Dolphin* dropped anchor beside the huge body of the white whale. The sailors cut him up and boiled the blubber for the sperm oil. In a few days the job was done, and they set sail for Nantucket.

"We're loaded to the hatches with oil. We'll all be rich," said Captain Skinner. He felt so happy that he danced a hornpipe across the deck. Tappy, tappy, tap, went his peg-leg.

Stormalong sat down on a hatch and rested his feet on the jib boom. He picked up his guitar and began to sing loud and gay.

"Twang, twang! Plunk, plunk! Plunkety, twang!" went the

guitar. The deep notes sounded like a pipe organ and the high notes were as sweet as violins. Stormalong sang *Home on the Range* and *Bury Me Not on the Lone Prairie*.

The crew came back with *Blow the Man Down*. Stormalong topped them with *As I Was Walking Down the Streets of Laredo*. Then they all chimed in with *Whiskey for My Johnnie*.

The sound of their ·music was so sweet that all the fish lifted their heads out of the water to listen. Sea gulls flew after the ship, beating their wings in time to the music. All the way across the ocean the fish followed the *Dolphin*. In schools and shoals and droves they came, and the New England fishermen caught the greatest catch of seafish that was ever caught in all history.

When the *Dolphin* got into Nantucket, the crew was

singing, each man-jack louder than the next:

> "Then give me a whaleman, wherever he be,
> Who fears not a fish that can swim the salt sea;
> Then give me a tight ship, and under snug sail,
> And last lay me 'side the noble sperm whale;
> > In the Indian Ocean,
> > Or Pacific Ocean,
> > No matter *what* ocean;
> > Pull ahead, yo heave O!"

When the crowd at the dock heard about Mocha Dick they gave such a shout that the clouds scattered clear out of the sky.

Stormalong waved to the crowd, and hurried to the Sailors' Snug Haven. He picked up the slate, on which were the words:

101

On this voyage of the Dolphin I will capture Mocha Dick.

Signed, Alfred Bulltop Stormalong

But the Great White Whale just laughed at him and spit in his eye.

"No more he doesn't!" shouted Stormalong. He smashed the slate into a thousand pieces. "Mateys," he roared, "I captured Mocha Dick. If I captured Mocha Dick, I'm a whaler. And if I'm a whaler, then I'm a sailor. And if I'm a sailor, my place is on the sea. And the sea is no place for a cowboy. I'll never wear my cowboy outfit again, even though it was made special. And you can lay to that!"

Then Stormalong sat down and ate twelve dozen oysters,

fifty-two codfish balls, sixty-seven lobsters, ten pounds of whale steak, a dory full of shark soup, and another full of clam chowder. For dessert he had a New England boiled dinner, three or four apple pies, and a nibble or two of maple-sugar candy. He washed it all down with a keg of New England rum, then hooted like a foghorn and whistled shrill like the wind in the rigging.

"Hooray for Old Stormalong!" shouted all the crew. "Hooray, hooray, *hooray!*"

After staying on shore for a week, Stormalong sailed off again on the *Dolphin*. He made many voyages in many ships, until Donald McKay built a ship called the *Courser*. She was so big that the captain and his officers had to ride around on horseback. The mast was so tall that it had to be bent back on hinges to let the sun and the moon go past.

When Stormalong saw the Courser he said, "There's my ship," and asked the captain for a berth.

But that's another story.

104

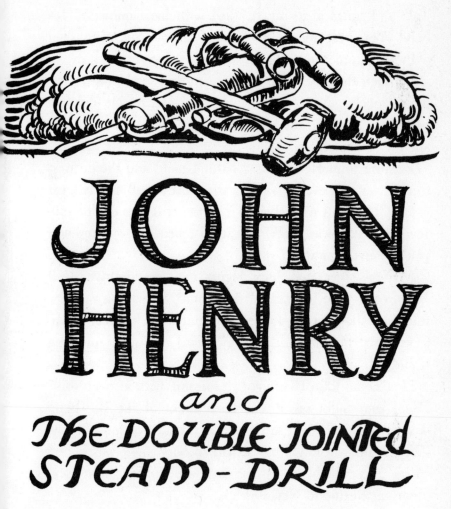

JOHN HENRY
and
THE DOUBLE JOINTED STEAM-DRILL

By

IRWIN SHAPIRO

WITH DRAWINGS BY JAMES DAUGHERTY

FOR a long time now there's been talk about John Henry. For a long time now there have been songs about John Henry. Talk and songs alike say he died with his hammer in his hand. Yes, beat the double-jointed steam drill, then died with his hammer in his hand.

No such thing! Couldn't any steam drill send John Henry to his lonely grave! No, sir! Not John Henry! He did feel poorly for a while, and weary and blue. But in the end he ran the steam drill right into the ground. That's a fact.

Because John Henry was a natural man, and the greatest steel driver that ever was. He was almost as tall as a box car is long. His arms were thicker than the cross-ties on the railroad. His skin was black, and it glistened like a brand-new pair of ten-dollar shoes.

My, my, how that John Henry man could drive steel! Why, each time he raised his hammer, it made a rainbow round his shoulder. And when he brought his hammer down, folks three hundred miles away heard an awful rumbling sound.

How come John Henry got to messing with a steam drill? Well, you might say it was on account of the Big Bend Tunnel. Or you might say it was on account of John Hardy. Then again you might say it had to happen—it was bound to be. Any which way, the fuss began on the night John Henry first came to New Orleans.

That night John Henry walked along, wearing his overalls and his clodhopper shoes. He meant to see the sights, and he did. First he had him a look at the houses with their little iron-railed balconies. Then he headed for the levee to cast his eyes over the steamboats. He hadn't gone very far, though, before he stopped.

"I declare," said John Henry. "I do declare."

The streets were just jam-packed full of folks. They all

had masks over their faces. They were dressed up as pirates
and devils and clowns and what-all.

John Henry stooped low and asked a clown, "Is it always
like this in New Orleans?"

"Ha! ha!" laughed the clown, thumping him with a stocking filled with flour. "As if you didn't know the Mardi Gras Carnival was going on!"

John Henry had never seen a town before, let alone a Mardi Gras Carnival. While he was trying to puzzle it out, the clown tugged at his sleeve.

"That's a fine get-up you have," said the clown. "But we'd better hurry or we'll be late. Come on!"

Shaking his head, John Henry followed the clown around a corner. A parade was coming down the street, led by the King of the Carnival on his golden throne. Behind the King were men carrying torches, and floats of dragons and giants. Bands blew music. The folks cheered and threw confetti over each other.

"Great day in the morning!" said John Henry.

And the next thing that happened, he was marching in the parade.

Anything John Henry did, he made up a song to go with
it. Now he started to strut and sing:

> Mardi Gras!
> Don't know what it means!
> But it's fine to be here
> In New Orleans!

The parade wound around town until it came to a big
ballroom. The folks rushed inside, pushing John Henry in,
too. He danced like the rest, tossing off a buck-and-wing that
had the folks yelling for more. He was just beginning a new
step when the clock struck twelve.

"Time to unmask!" shouted the King of the Carnival.

All the folks took off their masks. That is, all except John
Henry.

"You there!" said the King. "Twelve o'clock! Time to unmask!"

"S'cuse me, King," said John Henry. "I ain't got no mask."

109

"Then wipe that lampblack off! And take off your stilts, so we'll know who you are!"

"That's no lampblack, King," said John Henry. "And I'm not wearing any stilts, neither."

"You mean to tell me you're just naturally that way?" said the King.

"Yes, suh," answered John Henry. "I'm nothin' but a natural man."

The King reared back on his throne.

"Where you from, boy!" he roared. "What are you doing here?"

There wasn't another sound in the whole ballroom. The band had stopped playing. The folks had stopped dancing. Everybody was standing around, watching John Henry.

And John Henry said, "I'm from the Black River Country where the sun don't ever shine. I've picked the cotton till I could pick cotton in my sleep. I got an itch in my heel, so I traveled down to New Orleans to get me a job of work."

"Throw him out!" said the folks. "Put him in the chain gang! He's too uppety for his own good! Send him to the chain gang!"

"Just a minute!" said the King, holding up his hand. He turned to John Henry and said, "Look here, boy! You claim you're a country boy and came here to do a job of work. Think you could roust cotton?"

"Think I could, King," answered John Henry.

"All right," said the King. "Everybody out to the levee! Send for John Hardy and tell him to be at my steamboat! We're going to have some fun!"

As soon as they heard that, the folks streamed out of the ballroom. They piled into carriages, lighting torches so they could see what was going on. With John Henry walking beside them, they rode to the levee.

"Halt!" ordered the King when they reached the steamboat. He stood up in his carriage and called out, "John Hardy! John Hardy!"

"Comin', cap'n," said John Hardy, stepping out from the crowd.

This John Hardy was a big man, though not as big as John Henry. He was built a lot closer to the ground.

He had a voice like a bullfrog, and was dressed mighty fancy for a rouster. He wore a checked shirt, blue jeans, and a belt studded with rhinestones.

"This boy thinks he can roust cotton," said the King.

"Do tell," said John Hardy, giving the folks a wink. "Country boy, ain't he?"

John Hardy looked John Henry up and down.

He said, "Mmm. He got the heft, all right. He got the size. But it takes a man to roust this old cotton."

"That's me, then," said John Henry. " 'Cause I'm a natural man."

"Takes a man by the name o' John to roust cotton," said John Hardy.

"That's me again," said John Henry. " 'Cause my name is John Henry, and I'm proud of it."

"Huh!" said John Hardy. " 'Tain't you a-tall. It's me. I'm John Hardy, and I'm the best rouster on this here river."

Just then a pretty girl in a red dress spoke up.

"Don't pay him no mind, John Henry!" she said.

"You keep out of this, Pollie Ann," said John Hardy.

"Hush your big mouth," said Pollie Ann. "John Henry can roust cotton if he wants."

John Hardy threw back his head and laughed.

"Wantin' ain't doin'," he said. "And if I don't roust this country boy off his feet, I'll never hold a hook in my hand again!"

"Well, go to it!" said the King. "That's what we're waiting to see."

John Hardy nodded his head. He gave John Henry a rousting hook, and the two of them began to roust cotton. John

Henry rolled his bale to the gangplank and began to cross it.

"Roll that cotton, John Henry!" said Pollie Ann. "Roll it good!"

But as soon as John Henry set foot on the gangplank, it began to buck and spring. John Henry tromped down hard, and the plank sprang right back. John Henry tromped down even harder. The plank arched up high, heaving him head over heels into the air. And John Henry fell into the river with a mighty splash.

"Look at that country boy!" laughed the folks.

"What did I tell you!" said John Hardy.

But Pollie Ann called out, "Try again, John Henry! First time's the hardest!"

John Henry crawled out of the river, dripping wet. He walked up to the gangplank, put one foot on it, and tested its spring. Swaying back and forth, he sang:

> Roust that cotton
> But don't be a fool,
> 'Cause this gangplank kick
> Like grandpa's mule.
> Roust that cotton,
> Roust that cotton, oh!

Then John Henry rolled his bale, and this time he rolled it right. He strutted across the plank, rolling two bales to John Hardy's one.

"Look out, John Hardy!" said the folks. "Might be that John Henry can really roust!"

"Huh!" said John Hardy. "Let him try this."

Sinking his hook into a bale, he raised it to his shoulder. And he toted that bale faster than John Henry could roll. Halfway across the plank, though, his knees started to sag.

"Guess you need a little help," said John Henry.

He hoisted his own bale to his left shoulder. Then he put his hook under John Hardy's belt. He picked him up, bale and all, and hoisted him to his right shoulder. He cake-walked across the gangplank and dropped his load on the steamboat deck.

The folks laughed fit to bust. The King almost fell out of his carriage. Pollie Ann jumped up and down. As for John Hardy—well, he was just full of shame. He threw down his hook and ran off.

"No need to do that!" said John Henry. "There's room on this river for two good rousters!"

"Let him go," said the King. "Because you're a natural man and the best rouster I ever saw. You can stay in New Orleans, son, and work for me. You be here tomorrow morning, ready to roll that cotton."

"I'll be ready, King," said John Henry.

"He sure enough will," said Pollie Ann. "Because I'm going to fix him a snack to keep up his strength."

And while the folks went back to the ballroom, John Henry walked off with Pollie Ann.

After that John Henry rousted cotton every day. When he was through working, Pollie Ann would make him a snack of hog jowls, chittlin's, cracklin's, corn pone, side meat, and greens. John Henry liked Pollie Ann's cooking and he liked Pollie Ann. It wasn't long before they were married. They rented them a little house with a piano in it and settled down. Everything went along just fine, and it looked like John Henry would keep on rousting cotton till nobody knows when.

Then one night John Henry and Pollie Ann were in their house, sitting at the piano. While Pollie Ann tickled the ivories, John Henry sang. All of a sudden they heard a knocking at the door.

"Who's that?" called John Henry.

"Nobody else but me," said a bullfrog voice. And who should come walking in but John Hardy. He had on a brown box coat, a pearl-gray hat, and ox-blood shoes. He puffed away at a cheroot, and he said, "Evenin', Brother Henry!

116

Evenin', Miss Pollie!"

"Well, I declare," said John Henry. "I do declare. I'm sure enough glad to see you, John Hardy. And I'm sure glad you got no hard feelings. 'Cause I never did mean to roust you off the river."

John Hardy flicked some ash off his cheroot.

"Maybe so, maybe so," he said. "Of course roustin' is all right for a country boy. I was aimin' to leave the river anyway."

"Where you at now, John Hardy? What are you doin'?" asked John Henry.

"I'm drivin' steel on the railroad," said John Hardy. "I goes here, and I goes there—wherever they're layin' track."

"Drivin' steel," said John Henry slowly. "Sounds right nice."

"Glad to hear you say so," said John Hardy. Then he stepped close to John Henry and shouted, "'Cause I ain't forgot how you shamed me in front of the folks! And should you care to drive steel against me—well, there's a job in

117

Alabama right now. That's where I'll be."

And he walked out, slamming the door behind him.

"Drivin' steel," said John Henry, his eyes shining.

"You don't have to go," said Pollie Ann. "You doin' all right roustin' the cotton."

John Henry played a chord on the piano and sang:

> I can pick the cotton, and I can roust it, too,
> Yes, pick the cotton, and I can roust it, too,
> But drivin' steel is what I'd like to do.

"Then stop your moonin' around," said Pollie Ann. "You make yourself a pack of clothes and go."

That's just what John Henry did. He said good-by to Pollie Ann and set off for Alabama. When he got to the place where the railroad was laying track, work had already started. A crew of men was driving steel, and with them was John Hardy.

"Well, Long John," said John Hardy to John Henry, "so you think you can drive steel."

"Well, Short John," said John Henry, "it looks like a job for a natural man. And that's me."

"Huh!" said John Hardy, making believe he was trying to hide a laugh. He took John Henry to the foreman and he said, "Cap'n, here's a man thinks he can drive steel. But big as he is, I'm goin' to burn him out in no time."

"I don't care about burning anybody out," said the cap'n. "I just want to see those spikes in those rails. Your friend looks like he can handle a hammer, so go ahead."

John Hardy and John Henry each picked them up a nine-pound hammer.

And John Hardy roared, "Cap'n, give me a whole line of spike holders! Let 'em stand in a row and look out—'cause I'm goin' to drive on down and mash those spikes in fast!"

John Henry said quietly, "Cap'n, you just give me one spike

holder. That will be enough for me."

The cap'n gave the word to the spike holders, and a dozen of them lined up on one side of the track. John Hardy began driving in the spikes, and he went right down the line.

John Henry's one spike holder knelt at his feet. John Henry took a few practice swings with his hammer, then began to drive steel. After a little while he sang:

> This old hammer
> Ring like silver,
> Shine like gold, boys,
> Shine like gold.

And every time he raised his hammer, it made a rainbow round his shoulder. And when he brought his hammer down, it made an awful rumbling sound.

All the same, John Hardy was way ahead of John Henry. He went on mashing down the spikes, his arms pumping away.

"Hey, country boy!" he said. "Ain't you burned out yet? You sings pretty, but singin' ain't swingin', and that's what drives in this steel."

John Henry smiled and said to the cap'n, "Cap'n, I don't need any spike holder a-tall. You can put my holder to holdin' spikes for John Hardy."

"You're crazy, boy!" said the cap'n. "Nobody can drive steel without a holder."

John Henry just smiled. He put a handful of spikes in his mouth, the way a tailor does pins. He picked up two nine-pound hammers. Then leaning over the track, he spit out the spikes, one by one. And he drove in each spike with a couple of taps of his two hammers. It wasn't long before he'd left John Hardy far behind.

"Look at him go!" said all the steel drivers and spike holders. "That *is* a natural man! John Henry is a steel-drivin' man if there ever was one!"

119

As for John Hardy—well, he was full of shame. He threw down his hammer and ran off.

After that John Henry drove steel every day. He traveled
to almost every state of the Union, driving steel. He worked

for the B. & O. Railroad, and the C. & O. Railroad. He worked
for the Houston and Texas Central, the St. Louis Western,
the Mississippi, Kansas and Texas, and lots more. Wherever
he went, he sent for Pollie Ann. They'd live in a tent, and
Pollie Ann would fix him snacks of hog jowls, chittlin's,
cracklin's, corn pone, side meat, and greens. Everything went
along fine, and it looked like he'd drive steel on the railroad
till nobody knows when.

Then one day John Henry came walking into the tent and
said to Pollie Ann, "The C. & O. Railroad is buildin' the Big
Bend Tunnel in West Virginia."

"That's nice," said Pollie Ann.

"They'll be needin' men to drive steel," said John Henry.

Pollie Ann didn't say anything, so John Henry went on.

"It ain't like drivin' steel on the railroad," he said. "No,
suh. You got to push that ol' mountain down."

Pollie Ann whirled around.

"John Henry," she said, "has that no-'count John Hardy been here? Is that it?"

"Why, no! No, ma'am! I just heard the news is all," said John Henry.

"John Henry," said Pollie Ann, "you don't have to go. You doin' all right drivin' steel on the railroad."

John Henry hung his head. Pollie Ann gave him a long look, then said, "Well, don't stand here moonin' like a sick cow. You got your mind set on goin', so get along."

And John Henry did. He got together a little pack of clothes, and set out, singing:

> I'm a natural man, and I got to get around,
> I'm a natural man, and I got to get around,
> So good-by, Pollie, 'cause I'm West Virginia bound.

By the time John Henry reached West Virginia, the work had already started. The steel drivers were up on the mountain, driving steel. The turners and shakers were turning and shaking. The blacksmiths were putting new points on the jumpers. Walking among them all was the foreman, Cap'n Tommy Walters.

John Henry's shadow fell over the mountain, and everybody looked up.

"Great Gadfrey!" said Cap'n Walters. "Who are you, boy? Look like a regular giant."

"No, suh, cap'n," said John Henry. "I ain't no giant. I'm nothin' but a man, a natural man. I've been drivin' steel on the railroad, and now I'd like to do the same for you."

"Well, maybe," said Cap'n Walters. "But building a tun-

124

nel isn't like laying track. You've got to drive the steel jumper right into the mountain. You've got to drive her deep, so's we can put dynamite in the hole and blast out a tunnel. And she's a hard rock mountain, solid clear through."

"Suits me, cap'n," said John Henry.

"Well, you can try it," said Cap'n Walters. "You can have Li'l Willie there for a turner and shaker."

John Henry put down his pack of clothes and whipped off his shirt. He rubbed a little rock dust on his hands, and a little more on the handle of his hammer. He waited a minute while Li'l Willie knelt at his feet holding the jumper. Then he raised his hammer and began to sing. At the end of every line he sang, he brought his hammer down. It went like this:

> There ain't no hammer—clong!
> Upon this mountain—clang!
> Ring like mine, boys—bong!
> Ring like mine—whang!
> This ol' hammer—bom!
> Ring like silver—bam!
> Shine like gold, boys—whom!
> Shine like gold—wham!

And every time John Henry raised his hammer, it made a rainbow round his shoulder. And when he brought his hammer down, it made an awful rumbling sound.

"Look at that John Henry, cap'n!" said all the men. "Look at him whop that steel!"

They sang back at John Henry:

> If I could hammer
> Like John Henry,
> If I could hammer
> Like John Henry,
> Lawd, I'd be a man,
> Lawd, I'd be a man.

125

After that John Henry drove steel on the mountain every day. He sent for Pollie Ann, and they rented them a little house with a piano in it. When John Henry was through working, Pollie Ann would fix him a snack of hog jowls, chittlin's, cracklin's, corn pone, side meat, and greens. Everything went along fine, and it looked like John Henry would keep driving steel on the mountain till nobody knows when.

Then one day John Henry was hammering away, hammering away. The drivers alongside him were doing the same, and Cap'n Walters was saying:

"Come on, you bullies! Drive that steel! We've got to build the Big Bend Tunnel to let the trains run through!"

All of a sudden they heard a noise—chug-chug, chug-chug!

"Sound like the train comin' already," laughed John Henry. "Even before we got the track laid."

And chuggety-chug, chug-chug, something came scooting around the bend of the mountain. This little old something had a smokestack and wheels, and yet it wasn't a locomotive. It hissed and puffed steam, and yet it wasn't exactly a steam engine. Two men were riding on it. One of them was wearing a ten-gallon hat and a blue serge suit. The other had on a checked shirt, blue jeans, and a belt studded with rhinestones.

"Hello, Big Stuff!" he said in a bullfrog voice.

"I declare!" said John Henry. "I do declare! If it ain't John Hardy! Howdy, Small Stuff!"

"It's me, all right, Long John," said John Hardy.

"What's that you're sittin' on, Short John?" asked John Henry.

"A steam drill, Brother Henry—a steam drill," answered John Hardy. "She's new-fangled! She's triple-plated! And she's double-jointed! Yes, suh!"

"Sure enough?" said John Henry. "But what does she do?"

John Hardy opened his mouth to tell him, but the man in the ten-gallon hat jumped off.

"I'll take care of this," he said. He grabbed Cap'n Walters' hand and shook it. "Pleased to meet you, Mr. Walters. Just call me Breezy Sam. Ain't she pretty?"

"Well . . ." said Cap'n Walters.

"Glad you agree," said Breezy Sam. "Knew you would, though. This here double-jointed steam drill is the wonder of the age. She drills holes in the rock faster than any ten men can drive steel. And it only takes one man to handle her. Cap'n, two-three of these steam drills will get your tunnel through in no time."

John Henry stooped low to have a good look at the steam drill. John Hardy pulled a lever and blew steam in his face.

"Look out, boy!" shouted John Hardy. "She'll chew your head off if you ain't careful! I'm holdin' her back, but it ain't easy. So stand back before I drill this mountain out from under your feet."

John Henry looked at Cap'n Walters and the two of them let out a laugh.

The cap'n said to Breezy Sam, "You'd better peddle your contraption somewhere else, mister. As long as John Henry is driving steel for me, I don't need any steam drill."

"Huh!" said John Hardy. "Just let me run this little ol' steam drill against John Henry! Let me show him, Mr. Sam!"

"Why, can't any man stand up against the steam drill. Can't any man beat a machine," said Breezy Sam.

"How about it, John Henry?" asked Cap'n Walters.

"Cap'n," said John Henry, "a man ain't nothin' but a man, even if he is a natural man. But before I let that steam drill run me down, I'll die with my hammer in my hand."

"What do you say to a match?" said the cap'n to Breezy Sam.

They talked it over, and decided to hold a match the next day. The steam drill against John Henry, and the one that drove the deepest hole would win. If John Henry lost, the cap'n promised to buy some steam drills. If the steam drill lost, Breezy Sam would pay Cap'n Walters five hundred dollars.

"Well, tall boy," said John Hardy, "this is the time you ain't goin' to shame me before the folks."

"Well, small boy," said John Henry, "we'll see about that."

"We sure will, tall fry," said John Hardy.

"We sure enough will, small fry," said John Henry.

After that Cap'n Walters sent John Henry home to rest up for the match. When John Henry told Pollie Ann about it, she didn't like it a bit.

She said, "I wish that John Hardy would keep away. I don't like the idea of you messin' around with a steam drill."

All the same, she fixed him up a good snack, the way she always did. She even made some hot biscuits. John Henry ate hearty, then went to bed. He had him a good sleep and got up while it was still dark.

By the time John Henry and Pollie Ann reached the mountain the red morning sun was in the sky. Word about the race had got around, and a crowd had come from town to see the fun. Breezy Sam was standing by the steam drill, watching John Hardy get up steam.

The drivers and shakers cheered as they saw John Henry. None of them was going to work that day except Li'l Willie, and some blacksmiths to put points on the jumpers.

In a little while Cap'n Walters and Breezy Sam put their heads together. Then they called to John Henry and John Hardy both.

"Listen close," said Cap'n Walters. "When I give the signal, you start. At the end of twelve hours you'll stop. The one that drives the deepest hole in the rock wins. Now get set, and good luck."

"I don't need luck, cap'n," said John Hardy. "I got the steam drill."

"I don't need a steam drill," laughed John Henry. "I got my hammer."

John Henry whipped off his shirt. He rubbed some rock dust on his hands, and a little on the handle of his hammer. He waited until Li'l Willie had knelt at his feet with the jumper.

"Let 'er go, cap'n!" he said.

"Ready, cap'n!" cried John Hardy from the seat of the steam drill.

"Go!" yelled Cap'n Walters, and the match was on.

"Drive that steel, John Henry!" shouted Pollie Ann.

"Do it, John Henry!" said the drivers and shakers. "Whop that steel, brother! Mash it down, man!"

Some of the folks from the town cheered the steam drill.

"Beat him down, John Hardy!" they said. "Beat that John Henry down!"

The steam drill went *chug-chug* and John Henry sang:

> *Hear my hammer*
> *Ring like silver,*
> *Shake this jumper,*
> *Turn this jumper,*
> *I got a rainbow*
> *Round my shoulder,*
> *Soon we blow*
> *This mountain down.*

Both John Henry and John Hardy worked sure and steady. By the time the sun was shining bright, they were about even. Li'l Willie reached for a five-foot jumper and John Hardy changed his drill.

"How you feel, high pockets?" said John Hardy.

"Feel fine, low pockets," answered John Henry. "Just workin' up a sweat."

Breezy Sam yelled, "You, John Hardy! Show him a bit

130

of real speed! Let that double-jointed steam drill loose, boy!"

John Hardy let out the steam drill full blast, and that steam drill really began to drill. For a couple of minutes she chugged

131

away, then *bam!* she stopped. John Hardy had started it too fast and ruined a drill.

"Now's your chance, John Henry!" said Pollie Ann. "Get way ahead while he's changin' drills."

"That's just what I had in mind," answered John Henry. And he sang out to Li'l Willie:

> Come on, *Li'l Willie,*
> *Hold her steady,*
> *Turn her round,*
> *Shake her good.*
> *Let's beat that steam drill down,*
> *Lawd, Lawd, let's beat that steam drill down.*

Li'l Willie held the jumper steady. He turned her round and shook her good. And John Henry whopped it on down.

Breezy Sam's face was as red as a ripe tomato, while Cap'n Walters was just all smiles. But at last John Hardy got the steam drill started again, and he did it right. By the time the noonday sun was high in the sky, he was even with John Henry. Yes, he was even and inching ahead.

John Henry brought his hammer down so fast it threw sparks. Li'l Willie had to pour water on the jumper to keep it from getting too hot. Still, John Henry couldn't seem to gain on the steam drill. By the time the afternoon sun was blazing down, the steam drill was in the lead.

John Henry stood up straight and threw down his hammer.

"Great day!" roared John Hardy. "He's quittin' the race! I win!"

"You hush your big mouth!" said Pollie Ann. "John Henry ain't quittin' a-tall."

"That's right," said John Henry quietly, taking the head off his hammer. He pulled a long length of rawhide from his pocket and looped it through the hammerhead. Then he picked up a spare hammerhead, took out another length of rawhide, and did the same.

"Now, Li'l Willie," he said, "hold that jumper good and steady, 'cause I'm goin' to hammer in double-quick time."

And he started swinging those hammerheads by the rawhide, one in his left hand and one in his right. The two hammerheads came down on the jumper, ringing like a pair of bells.

John Hardy made his steam drill run as fast as he could. It shook and shivered, biting through the rock. Under the burning hot sun the steam drill drilled and John Henry drove that steel. And by the time the sun was red in the west, John Henry had caught up with the steam drill.

Then he stopped swinging those two hammerheads. He put one head back on the handle and began using one hammer again.

"How do you feel, son?" asked Cap'n Walters.

"Is your strength runnin' out, John Henry?" asked Pollie Ann.

John Henry shook his head and went on hammering. There wasn't any sound but the chug of the steam drill and the clang of John Henry's hammer. Everybody else was still— Pollie Ann and Li'l Willie, Cap'n Walters and Breezy Sam, the drivers and the shakers and the folks from the town. Because it was the flesh against the steam, the flesh against the steam. And a man was nothing but a man, and there was no telling how long John Henry would last.

"How come it so quiet?" said John Henry. He sang out, sweet and mellow:

> O my shaker, why don't you sing?
> For I'm throwing forty pounds from my hips on down,
> Just you hear that cold steel ring,
> That cold steel ring.

Li'l Willie started to sing, then stopped. John Henry was breathing hard now. He gave a little moan every time he raised his hammer. But he didn't leave off whopping that steel.

Pollie Ann whispered to Cap'n Walters, "How much time is left, cap'n? Look at your watch, cap'n, 'cause my John Henry's strength is running out."

"Half a minute to go," said Cap'n Walters, his eyes on his watch. "Quarter of a minute . . . ten seconds . . . five . . ." He raised his hand and shouted, "Time's up! The match is over!"

John Hardy stopped the steam drill. John Henry stood up straight, and his shadow stretched out long over the mountain.

The next minute the crowd let out a mighty cheer. They could see John Henry had drilled deeper into the rock. They gathered around him, cheering and laughing and carrying on.

"I knew you'd beat the steam drill!" said Cap'n Walters.

"We all knew it!" said the drivers and shakers.

John Henry looked down on them and smiled. He raised his hand and slowly passed it over his eyes. Then he crumpled up and fell to the ground.

"I said I'd beat the steam drill," he said. "But a man ain't nothin' but a man."

"Send for a doctor, Cap'n Walters!" cried Pollie Ann.

Before the cap'n could answer, John Henry's head fell back.

"No use to call a doctor," said Cap'n Walters quietly. "John Henry's gone, died with his hammer in his hand."

A chill wind blew across the mountain as the evening sun went down. All the men took off their hats. While Pollie Ann let out a great sob, they picked up John Henry. Walking slow, they carried him down to his little house. There wasn't any box big enough to hold John Henry, so they laid him out in a box car. They couldn't get the box car into John Henry's house, so they strung up a tent. And they left John Henry with Pollic Ann.

All night long Pollie Ann sat beside him. She lit a candle, and she had nobody to talk to but her shadow. She kept sobbing and saying, "It don't seem as if it could be. I can't believe John Henry ain't no more."

It was close to morning when she heard a little moan.

"Who's that?" she said.

After that she heard a little groan.

Pollie Ann turned her head, looking at the box car. And great day in the morning, if John Henry wasn't sitting up and raising his head! He was, and that's a fact!

"John Henry!" shrieked Pollie Ann. "You ain't dead!"

"Not so's I could notice it," said John Henry. "What caused you to think I was?"

Pollie Ann told him.

"I just threw me a faint," said John Henry.

"Mighty powerful faint," said Pollie Ann.

"I'm a mighty powerful man," said John Henry. "And when I faint, I don't faint puny."

He started to climb out of the box car, but Pollie Ann had to help him. John Henry wasn't dead, but he felt poorly. His strength was gone, and he was sort of sunken in and shriveled up.

Pollie Ann put him to bed and said, "Just rest yourself. You'll get back your strength in no time. I'll just call off the buryin'. I wonder could we turn it into a party, seein' that you're alive."

John Henry shook his head.

"No, ma'am!" he said. "Don't you do that, Pollie Ann!"

"Why not, John Henry?"

"Without my strength I ain't the man I was," said John Henry. "Why, if John Hardy was to see me this way, I'd never hear the end of it. I don't want to hear him laughin' 'cause the steam drill wore me down. You just let folks go on thinkin' I ain't on this earth no more. Then when I'm feelin' good again, I'll pick up my hammer and run John Hardy and his steam drill right into the ground."

Pollie Ann didn't like it. She didn't like making believe she was a widow woman and telling folks something that wasn't so. But she was so glad to have John Henry back she didn't want to cross him. While he ate the snack she fixed, she filled the box car with rocks.

"Put in plenty," John Henry said. "Weigh it down, so nobody will know I ain't inside."

Peeping through the window, he saw folks coming toward the tent. He told Pollie Ann to put on her black veil and stand beside the box car.

John Henry watched the folks streaming into the tent. Cap'n Walters was there, with Li'l Willie and the drivers, the shakers, and the blacksmiths. They all carried flowers to strew over him. John Hardy and Breezy Sam followed, with the most flowers of all. Then came folks from all over the town.

John Henry chuckled when he saw John Hardy's long face.

"I declare," he said. "That John Hardy is makin' out like he lost his best friend."

Pretty soon John Henry heard the folks singing *Swing Low Sweet Chariot* and *Deep River*. He sang right along with them. Then the preacher said a few words and John Henry listened.

138

"Sisters and brethern," said the preacher, "John Henry was a man. He was a big man and a natural man. Still, he wasn't nothin' but a man, and now he's gone. He's gone to where he won't ever have to drive steel no more."

"I ain't gone," John Henry said. "All the same, that's nice preachin'."

The tears came to John Henry's eyes as he listened to the preacher. He was still sniffling when the folks came out of the tent. Fifty of them wore white gloves and carried the box car on their shoulders. They put the box car on a wagon frame drawn by thirty-two black horses. They heaped it with flowers, then a band played slow music and the procession started on its way.

Soon as everybody was out of sight, John Henry crept from his bed. He went to the corner, where his hammer was leaning against the wall. He put both hands on the handle, but he couldn't lift it at all. No matter how hard he tried, he couldn't budge that hammer an inch.

John Henry shuffled over to the piano, feeling sad. He played a few chords and began to sing the weary blues:

I beat the steam drill, but see what it did to me,
Beat the ol' steam drill, but look what it did to me,
John Henry ain't the man he used to be.

He was still at it when Pollie Ann came back.

She took one look at him and burst out, "You, John Henry —you get back in your bed! No need to sing the blues. Just lay back easy while I fix you a snack. You'll fatten up and soon you'll be back on the mountain again."

"But what are we goin' to do? How we goin' to live?" asked John Henry.

"Well," said Pollie Ann, "I can't drive steel on the mountain. But I reckon I can drive steel where they're layin' track. I'll get me a job till you're on your feet again."

And that's just what she did. While John Henry lay on his bed, Pollie Ann drove steel like a man. As soon as she got home she'd fix John Henry a snack of hog jowls, chittlin's, cracklin's, corn pone, side meat, and greens. And John Henry began to fatten up. He began to get his strength back, too. Every day he tried to lift his hammer, and each day he could raise it a little more. And one day he found he could give it a full swing—not the way he used to, maybe, but better than anybody he knew.

"Just need a little practice," he thought.

Then he had an idea. He'd walk up the mountain and get his job back from Cap'n Walters. He'd surprise Pollie Ann and John Hardy and anybody else who happened to be around.

"It'll be just like old times," he chuckled.

So he put on his overalls and his clodhopper shoes. Shouldering his hammer, he set off for the mountain. He kept laughing all the way, figuring how everybody would be surprised.

But as John Henry climbed the mountain he heard a sound: chug-chug, chuga-chug. John Henry stopped. Although the sun was blazing down on his back, a little shiver ran through him. He climbed on slowly, rounded a bend, and stopped again.

"Oh, my," he moaned.

Because he didn't hear any hammers ringing on the steel. He didn't see any drivers or any shakers. All he heard was chuga-chug-chug. All he could see was steam drills working away. And handling the biggest, loudest steam drill was John Hardy.

"Cap'n Walters!" called John Henry softly.

Cap'n Walters wasn't around either. There was a new cap'n, and he said, "He's not here, son. What can I do for you?"

"Cap'n," said John Henry, "I'm John Henry and—"

The cap'n threw back his head and laughed.

"Boy," he said, "what are you telling me? You're big all right, but you're not John Henry. Everybody knows he died with his hammer in his hand. And if he hadn't died, he wouldn't be driving steel on this mountain. All we use now are steam drills. And even with the steam drills, we're having a hard time pushing through the Big Bend Tunnel."

"Thank you, cap'n. Good day, suh," said John Henry.

Without another word he started walking away. He stumbled across the ground like a man who's had too much rye whiskey. His shoulders sagged, and he sort of settled into himself, shriveled and shrunken up.

At the edge of a cliff he stood for a minute. He tossed away his hammer, watching it drop till it was out of sight.

"Good-by, ol' hammer," he said. "You won't never ring on the mountain no more."

John Henry kept on walking till he got to his house. He sat down at the piano and played and sang:

Oh, they're usin' steam on the mountain—can't deny it,
   'cause it's true,
Yes, usin' steam on the mountain—can't deny it, 'cause
   it's true,
Ain't nothin' left in the world for a natural man to do.

It was the meanest, weariest, saddest, low-down blues anybody had ever sung. When Pollie Ann came in John Henry asked her why she hadn't told him about the steam drills.

"I didn't know," she said. "Anyway, you can drive steel on the railroad."

"I couldn't do that," said John Henry. "Not after driving steel on the mountain."

"Well, then, you could roust cotton," said Pollie Ann.

"No," said John Henry. "Not after drivin' steel on the railroad."

"How about pickin' cotton?"

"Couldn't pick cotton," said John Henry. "Not after I rousted it on the Mississippi."

"John Henry," said Pollie Ann, "why don't you run one of these steam drills, then?"

John Henry shook his head.

"That's no work for a natural man," he said. "Don't take

145

a man to run a machine. Why, a machine's got no beat. You could never make up a song for it. No, there ain't nothin' left for a natural man, nothin' a-tall."

"What are you goin' to do?" asked Pollie Ann.

"Travel around," said John Henry. "Travel around, till I wear myself down and end out my days. 'Cause there's no place left in this world for a natural man no more."

So John Henry and Pollie Ann started traveling around. From West Virginia to East Virginia, to New Orleans, Kansas City, St. Louis, and Chicago. Kalamazoo, Louisville, Chattanooga, and Memphis—they went there too. They wandered and they rambled and they traveled around.

Nobody knew John Henry was John Henry. He got more shriveled up and shrunken in every day. He picked up a little

money working as a janitor, bellhop, or something like that. Pollie Ann worked too, as a cook or a maid. And whatever they did or wherever they went, John Henry never sang anything but the mean, weary, sad, low-down blues.

In Memphis John Henry and Pollie Ann both got jobs in a restaurant. John Henry waited on table, while Pollie Ann cooked snacks for the folks. Once in a while John Henry would walk over to the piano and sing a blues.

He'd just finished singing one day when he saw a man sitting in a corner. The air was blue with cigarette smoke, so John Henry couldn't make out his face. Anyway, he was hunched over the table with his head in his hands.

Walking over to him, John Henry said, "Anybody get your order? What would you like?"

"There's plenty I'd like," said the man. "But I can't eat a thing. I got the blues, just like you said in the song. Yes, sir— I got the John Henry blues, what I mean."

"What you got to do with John Henry?" asked John Henry.

"Ever hear of the Big Bend Tunnel?" asked the man, still holding his head in his hands.

"I heard tell of it," said John Henry.

"Well," said the man, "I've been runnin' a steam drill on the mountain, but I ain't runnin' it no more. The tunnel isn't even halfway finished, but the cap'n laid me off. Said he's goin' to get some real men to run those steam drills—men who can blow down a hard rock mountain. But I know he can't. Couldn't anybody push that mountain down but John Henry, and he's a long time gone."

Then he dropped his hands from his face, and great day in the morning, if it wasn't John Hardy! And that John Hardy looked hard at John Henry. He shook his head a little. He wrinkled his forehead. He rubbed his eyes and he looked again.

John Henry didn't waste any time. He ran to the kitchen, then through it, calling to Pollie Ann. Before they could reach the door, though, John Hardy caught up with them.

"John Henry!" yelled John Hardy. "I don't know how it came about! I know you ain't the same! But you're John Henry and you ain't dead! Yes, suh! And right beside you is Pollie Ann."

John Henry stopped and heaved a sigh.

"All right, John Hardy," he said. "I'm John Henry, and you've found me. Now go on and have your laugh."

John Hardy didn't even snicker. He just kept looking at John Henry and listened while Pollie Ann told what had happened.

148

"Just like a country boy," he said.

"Lookie here, small fry!" said John Henry.

"Huh!" said John Hardy. "You ain't such a big fry yourself no more. Now you listen to me. You've got to go back to West Virginia. You run one of those steam drills and push that mountain down."

"John Hardy," said Pollie Ann, "I always thought you was a no-'count big mouth. But now you talkin' sense."

But John Henry shook his head.

He said, "No, I ain't the natural man I was. And I couldn't run a steam drill. Why, a steam drill is a machine, and it ain't got no beat. I couldn't make up a song for it, let alone work it."

"You crazy, boy," said John Hardy. "A machine *has* got a beat. Only you never listened to it."

And then Pollie Ann really told John Henry off.

"John Henry!" she burst out. "You were too proud to let folks know you'd lost your strength, so I had to make believe I was a widow woman. Then you found out about them usin' steam drills, and you felt sorry for yourself. Now you're still a man, and there's always a place for a natural man. You beat the steam drill, but you ain't really licked it. That's what you got to do. Now get along."

"Maybe," said John Henry.

"No maybe about it," said Pollie Ann. "You get goin', and no foolin'."

John Henry looked at Pollie Ann, and he looked at John Hardy. He looked back at Pollie Ann again, and he said, "Yes, ma'am."

The very next minute he was on his way out of the café. Together with Pollie Ann and John Hardy, he traveled back to West Virginia. Every time they passed a factory with machines, John Hardy would get John Henry to listen. John

149

Henry put one hand behind his ear and heard the wheels go clackety-clack. He heard the motors go hum-hum-hum. He heard the pistons go pumpety-pump.

"I do declare," he said. "They sure enough got a beat."

And John Henry began to walk straighter and taller. By the time they reached West Virginia he was halfway back to his natural size.

In the dead of night John Henry and John Hardy climbed up the mountain. John Henry studied the steam drill, learning how it worked. John Hardy showed him how to fire the boiler, and they practiced drilling the rock. John Henry listened close as the steam puffed, the wheels turned, and the engine went chugety-chug-chug.

"I can't deny it," he said. "It's got a beat. It ain't like my ol' hammer ringin' on the steel, but I'm gettin' to like it."

Every day John Henry and John Hardy lay low, not letting anybody see them. Nights they practiced with the steam drill. And at last they were really ready to push through the tunnel. They just walked up the mountain one morning and John Henry started drilling away.

When the cap'n showed up he bellowed, "What do you think you're doin'? Get away from that steam drill! I never hired you! Come on, boy, before I get the law on you!"

"Go get the law, cap'n," said John Henry. "But before you do I'm goin' to blow this mountain down. 'Cause I'm John Henry, the natural man, and I'm goin' to push through this Big Bend Tunnel."

And he sang:

> There ain't no steam drill
> On this mountain,
> Can chug like mine, boys,
> Chug like mine.

150

This ol' steam drill
Chug like thunder,
Drill like lightnin',
Yes, indeed!

151

While the cap'n and all his gang watched with their mouths open, John Henry let out the steam full blast. He ran the steam drill just right, drilling faster, harder, and deeper than anybody before or since.

"Stand back, folks!" said John Henry. "Stand back, 'cause I'm a big man and gettin' bigger every minute! I'm a natural man, and I'm gettin' naturaler every second! Stand back, 'cause I'm goin' to blast this tunnel out in no time!"

Soon as John Henry drilled a hole, he and John Hardy filled it with dynamite. They blasted out the rocks and cleared them away in no time.

The cap'n sat back on his heels and scratched his head.

"Don't know if he's John Henry or not," he said. "Don't know if I should allow this or not. But no matter who, what, or why, this man can sure handle a steam drill."

All day long John Henry worked, stopping once to eat a snack Pollie Ann brought him. He blasted, he cleared away, and he drilled. He drilled and blasted and cleared away. Come night and he and John Hardy kept right on.

The stars shone out in the sky, but you couldn't tell them from the sparks that flew from the steam drill. The chug of the drill and the thunder of the blasting was heard for miles around. Folks listened, then hurried up the mountain to see what it was all about.

"Looks like John Henry," they said. "Couldn't be, though. Unless it's his ghost."

"Couldn't any ghost drill like that," said the cap'n. "And if that's not John Henry, that's John Henry's twin."

"That's John Henry, all right," said Pollie Ann. "And ain't he a natural man?"

At last the sky began to pale and the morning star to fade. John Henry drilled the last hole. He blasted the last blast. There was a great noise, and when the dust had cleared

everybody saw the tunnel had been pushed through. And
the folks sang:

> John Henry's back on the mountain,
> Though you can't hear his hammer ring,
> He's chugging away on a steam drill now,
> He's driving steel again.

> And every time that steam drill drills
> You can hear his cap'n shout,
> And every time that steam drill drills
> A thousand stars fly out.

> John Henry's built a tunnel
> For the locomotives and the cars,
> John Henry's back on the mountain,
> He's whoppin' out the stars.

John Henry asked John Hardy, "How'd I do, small fry?"
"Just fine, tall fry," answered John Hardy.
"Couldn't be finer," said Pollie Ann, and the cap'n said
the same.

All of a sudden they heard a noise. The steam drill was
puffing and panting, moaning and groaning. It shook and
shivered as if all its bolts were loose.

John Henry took a deep breath. He stood up tall, almost
as tall as a box car is long. He stretched his arms, and they
were thicker than the cross-ties on the railroad. In the light
of the rising sun his black skin shone like a new pair of ten-
dollar shoes.

John Henry looked hard at the steam drill, singing:

> I've laid aside my hammer,
> I say it just as plain,
> But I've run the steam drill into the ground
> And I'm a natural man again.

Just as John Henry sang the last note, there was a loud crash. Every nut, bolt and screw flew off the steam drill. While the folks laughed and cheered, it buckled up and fell down—because John Henry had run the steam drill right into the ground.

STEAMBOAT BILL

AND THE CAPTAIN'S TOP HAT BY

IRWIN SHAPIRO

PICTURES BY DONALD McKAY

You may think that the boilers of the *Whippoorwill* exploded and blew Steamboat Bill to bits. But they didn't. You may think that Steamboat Bill never did beat the record of the *Robert E. Lee*. But he did. Of course, he *almost* didn't, because of a little trouble he had with Captain Carter.

The whole thing started when the *Whippoorwill* came steaming into St. Louis one bright sunny day. And a grand sight the *Whippoorwill* was, with her white decks shining in the sun and her smokestacks spouting black smoke. Steamboat Bill was at the wheel in the pilot house, which is where a pilot should be. He had a big cigar in his mouth. His coat was open to show his fancy checked vest. His cap was perched on the back of his head, and his gray hair flew in the breeze. Anybody could see that he was a mighty man.

After the *Whippoorwill* rounded the bend, Steamboat rang the big brass landing-bell. With his other hand he pulled a lever, letting loose a blast of the five-toned whistle. Then he

put both hands on the wheel and eased the *Whippoorwill* up to the levee, as gentle as a mother with a baby.

"Prettiest landing I ever did see," said the second pilot. He was a young fellow with a big droopy mustache. His name was Sam Clemens.

"Thank you, Sam," said Steamboat. "Thank you kindly. But I guess the captain will be along soon with a different story."

And sure enough, there was Captain Carter striding toward them on the hurricane deck. He was wearing a tail coat and a top hat.

Now Captain Carter and Steamboat Bill were great friends. But at the end of every trip, they had a quarrel. If Captain Carter didn't start it, Steamboat did. They said it was the only way they could keep each other from getting swelled heads. To tell the truth, they enjoyed quarreling with each

other. And since they always made up afterward, no harm was done.

Captain Carter threw open the door of the pilot house.

"Pilot," he said, "now that the voyage is over, I've something to say to you."

"Say it quick and say it quiet," said Steamboat.

"I'll say it any way I like," said Captain Carter. "And this is what I have to say. Didn't you take that last bend a little too fast?"

"The law of these United States says that a captain cannot give orders to a pilot," answered Steamboat slowly.

"Only when the pilot is on duty," the captain came back, quick as a shot. "Anyway, laws be blowed! Did you or didn't you take that last bend too fast?"

"I'll answer to no captain, you thundering dunderhead!" shouted Steamboat.

"I'm a dunderhead, am I?" said Captain Carter. "Then you're a bomickle!"

"I'm a bomickle, am I?" said Steamboat. "Then you're a comickle!"

"So I'm a comickle, eh?" said the captain.

Steamboat shoved his face close to the captain's.

"Aye," he said. "You're a comickle."

"Enough of your sass!" burst out Captain Carter. And taking off his top hat, he threw it on the floor. "Kick that," he said, the way you would dare somebody to knock a chip off your shoulder. "Kick it and get what's coming to you. Go on, you ring-tailed baboon, give it just one little kick."

"I've a good mind to do that very thing," said Steamboat.

"That's just what I'm asking you to do."

"But I won't take orders from a captain!" roared Steamboat. "I wouldn't kick your hat if you left it there a million years!"

"In that case," said the captain, "I'll forget everything you said."

"And if that's the way you feel about it," said Steamboat, "I'll forget everything you said."

Captain Carter began to smile. Steamboat Bill began to smile. They shook hands, and pretty soon they were laughing and slapping each other on the back.

Sam Clemens came over to them with a handful of cigars.

"Have a cigar, gentlemen?" he asked.

"Thank you, Sam," said Steamboat, taking a cigar.

"Don't mind if I do," said Captain Carter.

The three of them stood there, laughing and smoking their cigars.

At last Steamboat said, "Well, gentlemen, I guess I'll look around a bit. I'll see you later at the Slocum House."

"Fine," said Captain Carter.

"Fine," said Sam.

Steamboat Bill left the boat and started walking along the levee. Boats were drawn up along the wharves. There was the *Natchez* and the *Tuscarora*, the *A. L. Shotwell* and the *Duke*

of Orleans. The *Natchez* was loading cargo. The rousters sang a song as they carried sacks of meal up the gangplank.

"Up sack, you gone! Up sack, you gone!" sang the rousters.

The chief mate shouted, "Hump yourselves, boys! Get those sacks on board!"

From all sides people called out to Steamboat.

"Hello, Steamboat!" they said. "How are you, Steamboat Bill? Good day, sir!"

"How's the river at Hat Island?" asked the pilot of the *Duke of Orleans*.

"How's the crossing at Memphis?" asked the pilot of the *Tuscarora*.

"How's the river at Twelve-Mile Point?" asked the pilot of the *A. L. Shotwell*.

"She's slack water all along," answered Steamboat Bill. "Couldn't get through the cut-out at Hat Island. The reef is showing at Twelve-Mile Point."

The pilots nodded.

"Steamboat knows the river like he knows the palm of his own hand," they said.

Steamboat smiled. He opened his coat to show his fancy checked vest. He pushed out his chest, pulled his cap over one eye, and puffed his cigar. Anyone could see that he was a mighty man.

Steamboat was still talking to the pilots when Captain Carter came running up. The captain's face was as long as a gangplank.

"What's the matter, Captain?" asked Steamboat.

"Have you heard the news?" said the captain. "There's trouble at Fort Sumter."

"That's bad," said Steamboat, frowning.

"That's bad," said all the pilots, and they shook their heads.

"Steamboat," said Captain Carter, "it means war. Civil war."

"Aye," said Steamboat. "Civil war."

For a long time no one spoke. Then Steamboat said, "Captain, are you with the North or the South?"

"I'm with the South," answered Captain Carter. "A state has the right to leave the Union."

"I'm with the North," said Steamboat. "The states must be united."

Steamboat and Captain Carter looked at each other.

"Good-by, Steamboat," said Captain Carter, holding out his hand. "And good luck."

Steamboat shook the captain's hand.

"Good-by, Captain," he said. "And good luck to you."

Then Captain Carter walked back to the *Whippoorwill*, and Steamboat Bill walked away from the levee.

It was a long time before Steamboat saw the captain again. But everything must come to an end, even wars. And so one bright sunny day, Steamboat hurried down to the levee at St. Louis to meet the captain.

As Steamboat hurried along, people called out to him from every side.

"Hello, Steamboat!" they said. "How are you, Steamboat Bill! Good day, sir!"

Steamboat smiled such a big smile that it almost hid his face.

"Hello, friends," he said. "I'm feeling very well. The civil war is over and Captain Carter is coming back on the *Whippoorwill*."

Steamboat opened his coat to show his fancy checked vest. He pushed out his chest and pulled his cap over one eye. Anyone could see that he was a mighty man.

Suddenly someone cried out, "Here she comes! Here comes the *Whippoorwill*."

Everyone ran down to the wharf to see the *Whippoorwill* come in. Carts and wagons clattered. Dogs barked. Boys whistled and yelled. When Steamboat saw the *Whippoorwill* steaming around the bend, he was so excited he could hardly stand still. Yes, there she was! Her white decks were as clean as a Dutch kitchen. Her brass-work shone in the sun like a new penny. Her five-toned whistle was blowing, and black smoke poured out of her smokestacks.

Kerplunk! Her gangplank hit the land, and a man in a white apron came running down. He was carrying a tray loaded with nuts, ices, grapes, pineapples and oranges.

"Compliments of the captain," he said.

The crowd rushed over to him. Soon there wasn't a thing left on the tray. Everyone stood around, munching and laughing.

"Where's Captain Carter?" asked Steamboat.

"He'll be here directly," said the man.

And sure enough, there was Captain Carter coming down the gangplank. He was wearing his tail coat and top hat. He walked straight up to Steamboat Bill.

"Well, Steamboat?" said Captain Carter.

"Well, Captain?" said Steamboat.

The next minute they were laughing and slapping each other on the back.

"It's good to see you again, Steamboat," said Captain Carter.

"You're a sight for sore eyes, Captain," said Steamboat. "And so is the Whippoorwill."

"She's a fine boat," said the captain proudly. "And soon you'll be at her wheel again. That is, if you still want to be my pilot."

"I wouldn't pilot for anyone else," said Steamboat, "and you know it."

Captain Carter gave Steamboat a tremendous thump on the back.

"And I wouldn't have anyone else for a pilot," he said. "Yes, sir, we'll both be back on the Whippoorwill again. It will be just like old times. You were for the North and I was for the South, but the war is over and we'll forget all about it."

"We won't even talk about it," said Steamboat.

"Not a word," agreed the captain. "The North won, and that's all there is to it. But I must say we gave you boys a battle at Bull Run."

"That's right. But we certainly had you on the run at Shiloh," chuckled Steamboat.

The captain laughed.

"You certainly did," he said. "But we beat you again at the second battle of Bull Run."

"We won at Vicksburg."

"Yes, but we whaled the tar out of you at Fredericksburg. And we fooled you at Chancellorsville."

"We won again at Gettysburg," said Steamboat.

"That's because you were lucky," said the captain.

"Lucky?" said Steamboat. "How about Missionary Ridge? I suppose we were lucky to win that one, too."

"Well, you would have lost if it hadn't been so foggy."

Steamboat was beginning to get angry.

"Next you'll be telling me that Grant didn't take Richmond," he said.

"Just luck, that's all," said the captain.

"Is that a fact?" said Steamboat.

"Yes, that's a fact!" shouted Captain Carter.

"And I suppose the South won the war!" Steamboat shouted back at him.

"We should have won!"

Steamboat looked the captain up and down.

"Captain Carter," he said, "you're a poor loser, that's what you are!"

"Shouldn't have lost!" shouted the captain.

"JOHNNY REB!" roared Steamboat.

"YANKEE!" roared the captain.

One of the men in the crowd said, "Gentlemen! This is no way to act."

"It's not my fault," said Steamboat. "This baboon wants to fight the war all over again."

"I'm not a baboon!" shouted the captain. "And I've stood enough!" And taking off his hat, he threw it on the ground. "Kick that," he said to Steamboat. "Go ahead. Just one little kick!"

"I've a good mind to do that very thing," said Steamboat.

"That's what I'm asking you to do."

"Then by the Great Horn Spoon, I will!" roared Steamboat. And he gave the captain's top hat a great kick. It sailed high into the air and fell into the river with a PLOP.

Captain Carter watched his top hat float down the river until it was out of sight.

"Steamboat," he said, "this is the end. You'll never pilot the *Whippoorwill* again. You're no friend of mine."

And with that Captain Carter walked up the gangplank.

"Steamboat, aren't you going to make up with the Captain?" asked someone in the crowd.

Steamboat pulled his cap down over one eye and lit a cigar.

"Captain Carter started this quarrel," he said, "and he'll have to end it. If he wants to talk to me, he knows where I'll be."

And he started walking toward the Slocum House.

WHEN Steamboat Bill left his room the next morning, he found a crowd of captains and owners waiting to see him. There was the owner of the *Eclipse* and the captain of the *Dexter;* the captain of the *Sultana* and the owner of the *Magnolia;* the captain of the *Southern Belle* and the owner of the *Belle of the West.* They all wanted Steamboat for a pilot.

They followed Steamboat down the hall. They walked with him down the stairs. They sat beside him as he ate his breakfast. Steamboat just shook his head.

"I guess Captain Carter will be along soon and ask me to come back on the *Whippoorwill,*" he said.

But Captain Carter didn't. He just kept the same pilot and took the *Whippoorwill* down to New Orleans.

"Oh, well," said Steamboat. "He'll come to see me on his next trip. He's a proud man and he has a temper, but he'll cool off."

The next time the *Whippoorwill* came to St. Louis, Steamboat hurried down to the levee. He stood where Captain

Carter would be sure to see him. But when the captain came down the gangplank, he walked past Steamboat as though he weren't there at all.

The same thing happened on the *Whippoorwill*'s next trip, and on the trip after that.

"You'd better get yourself another job," the captains and owners told Steamboat. "Captain Carter's temper is worse than ever. He throws down his top hat ten times a day. His temper is so bad that no pilot wants to work for him. The only pilots he can get are Caleb Smith and Jim Johnson."

"Why, Caleb Smith is so old he can hardly get around," said Steamboat.

"That's right," said the owners and captains.

"And Jim Johnson is just a youngster," said Steamboat.

"That's right," said the owners and captains.

"In that case," said Steamboat, "I guess Captain Carter will soon ask me to come back on the *Whippoorwill.*"

But Steamboat was wrong. Captain Carter didn't even say hello to Steamboat when he saw him on the levee.

Steamboat felt so bad that he never went down to the levee again. He stayed in his room all day. He would look out the window at the clouds of black smoke floating across the city. When he got tired looking out the window he listened to the bells and whistles of the boats on the river. When he was tired of listening, he read the newspaper. And when he was tired of reading the newspaper, he looked out the window again.

Then came the day when the *Natchez* and the *Robert E. Lee* finished their race from New Orleans. Steamboat was looking out the window, as usual. He could hear the crowds cheer as the *Robert E. Lee* came steaming up the river.

A man ran down the street and shouted to Steamboat, "She broke the record! She made it from New Orleans in

174

three days, eighteen hours, and fourteen minutes!"

Steamboat slammed down the window.

"It should have been the *Whippoorwill* that broke the record," he said. Then he sighed, "But there's nothing I can do about it."

He tried not to hear the cheers of the crowd at the levee. He sat down and put his head in his hands. He was sitting that way when there was a knock at the door.

"Go away!" said Steamboat. "I don't want to see anybody!"

"This isn't anybody," said a voice. "This is Sam Clemens."

"Sam Clemens!" said Steamboat, and threw open the door. "Come in, Sam. How are you?"

"Fine," said Sam Clemens. "How are you, Steamboat? Here, have a cigar."

"Thank you kindly," said Steamboat. He puffed his cigar, smiled at Sam, and said, "What have you been doing since

you stopped being a pilot?"

"Oh, I've been working on a paper and writing stories."

"Hm," said Steamboat. "It seems to agree with you. You look fine. And your mustache is bigger than ever."

"Funny thing about the mustache," said Sam. "I don't like it. Never did like it. I cut it off every night before I go to bed. But as soon as my eyes are closed it sneaks back on me. When I get up in the morning, there it is, sitting under my nose and laughing in my face."

"Sam," said Steamboat, "that's a funny story, but I can't laugh at it. I don't feel much like laughing. I guess you know why."

"I guess I do, Steamboat," said Sam. "But I have some news for you. Captain Carter is going to race the *Whippoor-will* against the *Thunderbolt*. He says he's going to beat the record of the *Robert E. Lee*."

"What!" shouted Steamboat. He was so angry that he

threw his cap on the floor and kicked it across the room. "The *Whippoorwill* will never win that race. She's a mighty boat, but she has to be handled just right. And Captain Carter has such a temper that he can't get a good pilot. But I guess there's nothing I can do about it." And he sighed.

Sam pulled his mustache and puffed out a cloud of smoke.

"Steamboat," he said, "stop that sighing. You're going to New Orleans and you're going to get on board the *Whippoorwill.* I don't know how you'll do it, but you will. You're going to teach Captain Carter a lesson, and you're going to break the record of the *Robert E. Lee.* And if you don't, you're no friend of mine."

Sam jammed on his hat and left the room. Steamboat stared after him. He shook his head. Then he scratched it. Then he shook it again. After that he started to smile

"By the Great Horn Spoon, I'll do it," he said. "I'm a mighty man and I'll do it. I'm Steamboat Bill, and I'm going to beat the record of the *Robert E. Lee.*"

Two weeks later Steamboat was walking down the levee at New Orleans. It was night, and a big yellow moon shone in the sky. The river was full of little golden dots and ripples. Steamboat listened to the water slapping against the shore, and took a deep breath of the river air.

"Nothing smells as good as a river," he said. "And there's no river that smells as good as the Mississippi."

He walked along the levee until he came to the *Whippoorwill*. Her white decks glistened in the moonlight, and her smokestacks stood up black against the pale sky.

"Aye, she's a mighty boat," said Steamboat, "and she's going to beat the record of the *Robert E. Lee*."

The *Thunderbolt* was at the wharf next to the *Whippoorwill*. Steamboat looked her over.

"She's a nice boat, too," he said, "but she'll never beat the record of the *Robert E. Lee*." Then Steamboat bent down and picked up a stone. He drew back his arm and threw the stone at the far end of the *Whippoorwill*. It fell on the deck with a bump.

"Who's there?" shouted the watchman on the *Whippoorwill*. And picking up his lantern, he ran across the deck to see what had made the noise.

"I knew that would get him," chuckled Steamboat. He walked up the gangplank and slipped into the cabin. He opened the door of a stateroom and went in. Then he lay down on the bunk for a little nap.

When Steamboat woke up it was afternoon. Outside the rousters were loading the last of the cargo. As they carried bales of cotton up the gangplank, they sang, "Lift dat cotton, hop! Lift dat cotton, hop!"

"Hump yourselves, boys!" sang out the chief mate. "Get that cotton on board. We've a race to run today!"

Steamboat went to the window and looked out. There were people everywhere—standing on the levee, sitting on rooftops, leaning from windows. Clouds of black smoke floated out from the *Whippoorwill's* smokestacks.

The chief mate shouted, while the rousters sang, "De las' sack! De las' sack!" Bells clanged and whistles blew.

Steamboat drew back his head as Captain Carter came hurrying by. With him were old Caleb Smith and young Jim Johnson. Caleb hobbled along on a cane. Jim's face was pale. The captain himself looked worried and anxious.

"Won't they be surprised!" chuckled Steamboat, and stuck his head out again.

Just then two cannons boomed. A great shout went up from the crowd as the *Whippoorwill's* crew gathered on the forecastle. One of the crew, dressed in a red shirt, waved a little flag. The crew began to sing:

"Ring, bells, ring!
Blow, whistle, blow!
Up the muddy Mississippi,
Up the river we go."

On the *Thunderbolt* the crew were singing:

"Roll, river, roll!
Roll, river, roll!
Steamboat comin' round the bend,
Steamin' toward the journey's end,
Roll, river, roll!"

With a blast of whistles, the *Whippoorwill* and the *Thunderbolt* began to move up the river. Their engines puffed and chugged. Their paddle wheels churned the water. Steam hissed.

"Hooray!" shouted the crowd, and threw their hats in the air. "Hooray for the *Whippoorwill!* Hooray for the *Thunderbolt!* Hooray!"

The *Thunderbolt* made a big curve and headed up the river. The *Whippoorwill* started to make a curve too, but suddenly it went scooting across to the opposite bank. By the

time the pilot got her headed straight again, the *Thunderbolt* was out of sight. The crowd on the levee roared with laughter.

"Careful, old Caleb!" they shouted. "Careful, young Jim! Watch your top hat, Captain Carter!"

Steamboat had to laugh, too.

"I guess the pilot is a little excited," he said. "And Captain Carter must be as angry as a wet hen. But never fear. Steamboat Bill will soon be at the wheel, and we'll beat the record of the *Robert E. Lee!*"

All day long Steamboat sat in the stateroom, smoking one cigar after another. The *Whippoorwill* chugged and churned and chuffed up the river, but the pilot just couldn't get speed out of her. It began to look as though she never would catch up with the *Thunderbolt*. When night came the *Whippoorwill* picked up a raft loaded with wood for the furnace.

"It's time for me to give Captain Carter a little surprise," said Steamboat. He stood up and opened his coat to show his fancy checked vest. He pushed out his chest and pulled his cap over one eye. Then he left the stateroom and made his way to the pilot house.

Steamboat saw young Jim Johnson walking along the hurricane deck. He reached out his hand and touched Jim on the shoulder.

"Good evening, Jim," said Steamboat.

Jim whirled around.

"Steamboat Bill!" he said, his eyes popping out of his head. And without waiting for another word, he jumped overboard and started swimming for shore.

"I must have given the lad a fright," said Steamboat, and went into the pilot house. Old Caleb Smith was at the wheel.

"Good evening, Caleb," said Steamboat.

Caleb cupped a hand over his ear.

"Eh?" he said. "What say? You'll have to speak louder. Who is it?"

"It's Steamboat Bill," said Steamboat Bill in a loud, clear voice.

Caleb put on his spectacles and stared into Steamboat's face.

"Why, so it is," he said. "I'm mighty glad to see you,

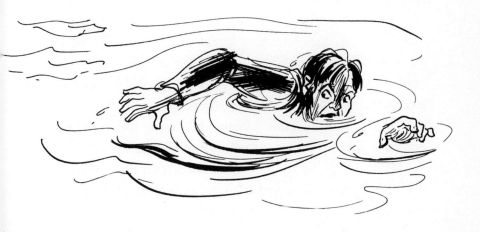

Steamboat. Maybe you can help me. I'm too old to handle the *Whippoorwill* and Jim Johnson is too young. We should never have come on this trip. You're the only man can handle the *Whippoorwill* the way she ought to be handled."

"Thank you kindly," said Steamboat. "And now, Caleb, if you want me to take the wheel and win the race, I'll tell you what to do. Get on the raft and get to shore. Don't let Captain Carter see you."

"I'll do that thing," nodded Caleb. He shook Steamboat's hand, wished him luck, and hobbled away.

"Now then," said Steamboat, taking the wheel. He peered out at the river and rang for full speed ahead. He steered the *Whippoorwill* a little closer to shore.

"We're near Rat-tail Island," he said, "and the current close to shore is better for us. Especially the way the river is rising."

The *Whippoorwill* began to pick up speed.

"Ah," said Steamboat, "that's better."

Soon the texas-tender came in with some hot coffee.

"Steamboat Bill!" he shouted. "You're back! Hooray!" He ran out to tell the crew that Steamboat was at the wheel of the Whippoorwill again.

Steamboat sipped the hot coffee and smiled.

"I guess Captain Carter will be along soon," he said.

And sure enough, there was Captain Carter hurrying toward him on the hurricane deck. He was wearing his tail coat and top hat. He burst into the pilot house, and glared at Steamboat. "Good evening, Captain," said Steamboat. "Fine evening. Just right for a race."

"What's the meaning of this!" shouted Captain Carter.

"Before you say anything else, I want to remind you of

one thing," said Steamboat politely. "The law of these United
States forbids a captain from giving orders to a pilot."

"You're no pilot of mine!" roared the captain. "Get off
this boat! Where's Caleb Smith? Where's Jim Johnson?"

"They're both on shore, Captain," said Steamboat. "And
I'm your pilot now, whether you like it or not."

Captain Carter looked as though he were going to burst.
But he knew it was against the law for a captain to give orders
to the pilot. He rushed out on the hurricane deck and
jumped up and down with rage.

"A fine crew I've got!" he shouted. "A fine mate I've got!

Fine deck hands! Fine watchmen! Call yourselves river men? You're a bunch of baboons, that's what you are! Letting Steamboat sneak on board! Letting Caleb Smith and Jim Johnson sneak off board! You're a pack of ring-tailed baboons!" He took off his top hat and threw it on the deck. "Kick that!" he bellowed. "Come on, any of you! Give it just one little kick. I'll knock the stuffing out of the whole crew!"

"Easy, Captain," said one of the deck hands. "We'll win this race now that Steamboat Bill is at the wheel! He's a mighty man, and he knows the river like he knows the palm of his own hand."

Captain Carter picked up his hat.

"All right," he said. "Don't mind me. Run the boat to suit yourselves. Just go ahead and do what you want. But if Steamboat Bill gets you into trouble, don't come running to me."

He sat down on a coil of rope and folded his arms.

"Just go ahead," he said. "Do as you please. You'll be sorry."

ALL that night and all the next day Steamboat steered
the *Whippoorwill* up the Mississippi. She was making real
speed, but still she couldn't catch up with the *Thunderbolt*.
When they got to Hat Island, Steamboat ordered the leadsman to make soundings.

"Mark Twain!" sang out the leadsman. "M-a-r-k twain!
Quarter twain! Mark three! M-a-r-k thre-e-e-e!"

"Just as I thought," said Steamboat. "The river is rising.
The floods are coming down the Mississippi. I'm going to
try the cut-out at Hat Island. If we can make it, it will save us
miles."

Steamboat headed the boat toward the cut-out. The water
was rushing between the shore and Hat Island with a terrible
roar. In the pale light of the sunset the water looked dark
and fearful. It boiled and bubbled, it rushed and roared.

Steamboat called for more steam.

"You see!" cried Captain Carter. "He's going to go up the cut-out. We'll never make it! We'll all be drowned! What did I tell you!"

Nobody listened to the captain. The crew kept throwing wood on the fire in the furnace, trying to get up more steam.

Steamboat pushed his cap on the back of his head. He gripped the wheel firmly and took a long puff on his cigar. Anybody could see that he was a mighty man.

"Stand firm, lads!" he shouted. "Here we go!"

The Whippoorwill shook from stem to stern as she plunged into the cut-out. The engines moaned and groaned and hissed steam. The paddle wheels thrashed the water. But before she could get through the cut-out, the current caught her. The Whippoorwill began to spin around and around like a top.

"I knew it!" howled Captain Carter. "What did I tell you? It's the end! Steamboat Bill will kill us all!"

But Steamboat steered the boat around carefully and they

slid back out of the cut-out.

"Boys," said Steamboat to the crew, "we can make it but I'll need more steam."

The engineer shook his head. "We've used up all our wood, Steamboat," he said.

"Then chop up the furniture!" said Steamboat. "Chop up the chairs! Chop up the tables! Chop up all the woodwork! But give me more steam, for I'm Steamboat Bill and I'm out to beat the record of the *Robert E. Lee!*"

"You'll ruin my boat!" shouted Captain Carter. But the crew cheered. With axes and hatchets they chopped up the gilt chairs from the dining room. They broke up the mahogany tables. They ripped out the doors. They smashed bedsteads. They even tore up part of the floor. They chopped everything into kindling wood and built the biggest fire that ever was in the furnace of a steamboat. Higher and higher

went the flames, while the furnace glowed ruby-red. And the steam began to rise in the boilers.

"The boiler will explode!" said Captain Carter. "We'll all be blown to bits! We'll be drowned! I told you so! I told you so!"

One of the deck hands said, "Maybe we'll all be blown to bits. Maybe we'll all drown. But Steamboat Bill is the mightiest man on the Mississippi, and I'd just as soon drown with him as with anybody else."

"Thank you kindly," said Steamboat. He lit another cigar, gripped the wheel, and called for full steam ahead.

The crew threw more wood on the fire. Billows of smoke rolled out of the smokestacks. Sparks flew out like flying stars. The blaze of the furnace threw a red and yellow shine on the river. And the steam rose in the boilers.

Steamboat headed the *Whippoorwill* up the cut-out again. She went up a little way, then stopped.

Captain Carter jumped up and down with glee.

"I told you so!" he said. "I knew it! I warned you! The

boilers are going to explode! We'll all be drowned! Maybe next time you'll listen to your captain instead of a good-for-nothing pilot!"

Steamboat edged the boat a little to one side. He turned the wheel just the tiniest bit, and the Whippoorwill pulled clear of the current. Chugging and hissing, the Whippoorwill shot forward and sped up the cut-out. Her paddle wheels cut into the water. She went so fast that she almost flew in the air. If she would have gone any faster, the crew would have had to throw out an anchor to keep her in the water.

"Hooray!" shouted the crew. "We made it!"

"The race isn't over yet," grumbled Captain Carter. But he

thought to himself, "Maybe we *will* beat the record of the *Robert E. Lee*. Steamboat Bill is a stubborn baboon, but he's the mightiest pilot on the river."

The *Whippoorwill* went by the *Thunderbolt* like a hurricane. The *Thunderbolt's* crew heard a roar, felt a wind on their faces, and that was all.

"What was that?" asked the captain of the *Thunderbolt*.

"What was what?" asked his chief mate.

"I don't know," said the captain. "But it was something."

The *Whippoorwill* went steaming and roaring around the bend at St. Louis. Before anyone could say, "Here she comes," she was at the levee. Steamboat had to reverse the engines to get her to stop. Then he pulled the lever of the five-toned whistle. As the steam came rushing through the whistle, it let out a terrific blast. It was heard down the river as far as New Orleans, and up the river as far as Bemidji, Minnesota.

The crowd on the levee cheered and whistled and shouted and yelled. Steamboat Bill came out of the pilot house. He opened his coat to show his fancy checked vest. He pulled

193

his cap down over one eye and pushed out his chest. Anyone could see that he was a mighty man.

When the crowd saw him they cheered louder than ever.

"Hooray!" they said. "Hooray for Steamboat Bill! Hooray for the *Whippoorwill!* Hooray for Captain Carter! They beat the record of the *Robert E. Lee!*"

Captain Carter walked up to Steamboat. He walked slowly and he looked ashamed.

"Well, Captain?" said Steamboat.

"Well, Steamboat?" said the captain.

Steamboat Bill began to smile. Captain Carter began to smile.

The next minute they were shaking hands and slapping each other on the back.

"Steamboat," said the captain, "you're the mightiest man on the Mississippi. And I'm a stubborn old dunderhead. And a bomickle and a comickle as well. Also a ring-tailed baboon."

Captain Carter took off his top hat and threw it on the deck.

"Kick that," he said to Steamboat. "Go ahead. Kick it into the river."

Steamboat shook his head.

"Then I'll do it myself," said Captain Carter. And he gave

the top hat such a kick that it went sailing out into the river.

Steamboat Bill and Captain Carter walked down the gang-plank together. The crowd cheered and cheered as though it would never stop. All the steamboats at the levee blew their whistles. A brass band played "Hail to the Chief."

Then a man with a big droopy mustache pushed his way through the crowd. It was Sam Clemens.

He slapped Steamboat Bill on the back. He slapped Captain Carter on the back. He shook hands with them both.

"I knew you would beat the record of the *Robert E. Lee*," he said.

"Sam, I would never have done it if it hadn't been for you," said Steamboat. "It was your idea that put me on the *Whippoorwill*, and I'll never forget it."

Sam Clemens smiled. He reached in his pocket and took out a handful of cigars.

"Have a cigar, gentlemen," he said.

"Thank you kindly, Sam," said Steamboat, taking a cigar.

197

"Don't mind if I do," said Captain Carter.

Then, arm in arm, Steamboat and Sam and Captain Carter walked away from the levee.

JOE MAGARAC
and his
U*S*A CITIZEN PAPERS

by IRWIN SHAPIRO
PICTURES by James Daugherty

IF ANYBODY asks, "Who was the greatest steelman that ever was?" you say, "Joe Magarac." And you'll be right, by golly! Because he was the best feller for making steel in the whole world.

Yoh! That Joe Margarac, he was a real steel man. He was born on an ore mountain in the Old Country. He was even made of steel himself. Sure Mike—he was solid steel all over.

He was a big feller, too. Not so big high, maybe. Only seven or eight feet tall, about. But he was as big around as the smokestack on the steel mill. His arms were as strong as steel rails. His fingers were stronger than any other man's arms. He could never get a hat big enough, and he wore Size 18 extra-special wide-last triple-soled safety-toe shoes. Oh, he was one fine, big, strong feller.

Now some people will tell you that Joe Magarac was melted down into steel again. That was the end of Joe Magarac, they say. And he never did get his U.S.A. citizen papers.

Ho! They mean Joe Somebody-else, maybe. They don't mean Joe Magarac. They couldn't. Because Joe Magarac did get his U.S.A. citizen papers. After that, he made plenty steel for the U.S.A. You betcha your life!

Sure, he got a little bit rusty and had an accident. Sure, he fell into the ladle and was melted down. But before you hear how that happened, you have to hear about Steve Mestrovich. You see, nobody ever knew about Joe Magarac until Steve Mestrovich's party at Plotsky's farm.

So we'll start with Steve Mestrovich.

O.K. Maybe fifty, sixty, hundred years ago, Steve Mestrovich was living in the town of Braddock, Pennsylvania, U.S.A. Steve was only a little feller, but he was as proud as anything. He was proud of his bushy mustache. He was proud of being a U.S.A. citizen. He was proud of being the best cinderman in the steel mill. He was proud of the way his missus cooked. He was proud of his little house on a hill, where he could look down and see the steel mill in the valley. Most of all, he was proud of his daughter Mary.

201

This Mary, she was the prettiest girl in the Monongahela Valley. She had big blue eyes and goldy hair, and she could dance the polka better than anybody. All the young fellers wanted to marry her. Mary liked Pete Pussick best of all. But whenever she talked of marrying him, Steve shook his head.

"Mary," he said, "you are prettiest girl anywhere. You are daughter of me, Steve Mestrovich, best cinderman in steel mill. When you get married, you gone catch best and strongest man for hoosband."

Mary always answered, "Pete Pussick is plenty strong feller."

"I don't know about that," said Steve. "Maybe pretty soon a feller comes along who is stronger as Pete Pussick. You wait awhile, Mary. I gone have strongest man in world in my fambily."

Steve's missus folded her arms and gave Steve a look.

"Better you not be such a Smarty Aleck, Mr. Steve Mestrovich," she said.

Steve winked one eye, pulled his mustache, and snapped his red suspenders.

"Ho!" he said. "You do like I tell you. Everything gone be O.K."

So Mary waited and waited. The trouble was, no other feller came along. Everybody was getting tired of it—even Steve. But he was too proud to change his mind.

One night, though, Steve was sitting in the kitchen of his house. He was smoking a pipe, while Mary and his missus put away the supper dishes. All of a sudden there was a knock at the door—bang! bang!

Steve opened the door, and there stood a whole crowd of young fellers. Pete Pussick from Braddock, Eli Stanoski from Homestead, Andy Dembroski from Johnstown—and a lot more. They all had fresh shaves and haircuts, and smelled pretty like a barbershop. Some of them carried big boxes of candy and some carried bunches of flowers. Pete Pussick carried a box of candy *and* a bunch of flowers.

"By golly, what is this?" asked Steve. "You all come to see Mary at one time?"

Pete Pussick took off his hat, very polite.

He said, "Mr. Mestrovich, we all bring present for Mary. But we come to see you."

"Well," said Steve, "I am standing right here. If you look, you see me."

All the young fellers gave Mary the candy and the
flowers. Then Pete Pussick cleared his throat—ahum!—and
said, "Mr. Mestrovich, for two years I come to see Mary.
Eli Stanoski, same thing. Andy Dembroski, same thing.
Other fellers, same thing. When we talk to you about wed-
ding, you always say Mary gone wait to catch hoosband
who is the strongest man anywhere. Now it is time for her
to make up her mind."

"That is right," said Eli Stanoski. "And if you want
strongest man for Mary's hoosband, don't you worry any
more. Because that man is me."

"Ha!" laughed Andy Dembroski. "Eli Stanoski is good man to make talk with the mouth. But when it comes to work, that is another thing. Everybody knows I am strongest man in Johnstown mill."

"Ho!" said Pete Pussick. "Best man in Johnstown is worst man in Braddock. You want to see really strong man? Looky!"

And he picked up the icebox to show how strong he was.

"That is nothing!" yelled Eli Stanoski, picking up the stove.

"I'll show you some real muscle!" shouted Andy Dembroski. With one hand he picked up a chair with Steve's missus sitting on it.

"I'll show you both!" said Pete Pussick.

"Is that so?" said Eli Stanoski.

"You will, will you?" said Andy Dembroski.

"You betcha my life!" said Pete Pussick.

Now all the young fellers were hollering and picking up furniture. Mary giggled.

Steve's missus screamed, "Put me down!"

Steve yelled, "Don't broke up my house!"

The neighbors heard the noise and came running over.

"What is going on here?" they asked.

Pete Pussick and Eli Stanoski and Andy Dembroski all tried to answer at once. So did Steve and his missus and Mary. Everybody was making so much noise nobody could hear anybody.

At last Steve jumped up and down and gave a big holler.

"Hey!" he said. "Checkai! Stop! Shut up, everybody! And put down that furniture or I gone throw you out!"

When it was quiet again, he said, "By golly, I am tired hearing every feller say he is right man for Mary's hoosband. I gone have strongest man anywhere in my fambily, you betcha."

"That is what you always say," said Pete Pussick.

"Sure Mike," answered Steve. "But I joost have good idea. This Sunday I will give party at Plotsky's farm in country. Everybody come. We will have contest to find out who is really strongest man. And that feller will be hoosband for Mary."

Steve's missus folded her arms and gave him a look.

"Better you not be such a Smarty Aleck, Mr. Steve Mestrovich," she said. "What kind contest you gone have?"

Steve winked one eye, pulled his mustache, and snapped his red suspenders.

"You will see," he said. "Everything gone be O.K."

As soon as the fellers left, Steve began to get things ready for the party. He went to Pittsburgh, where he ordered two barrels of beer from the brewery. Mary helped his missus make prune jack to drink and cakes to eat. They made big pots of polnena kapusta—meat and rice wrapped in cabbage leaves.

All week everybody talked about who was going to be the strongest man. Braddock people said Pete Pussick. Homestead people said Eli Stanoski. Johnstown people said Andy Dembroski. They all wondered who would be Mary's husband.

Come Sunday, Steve and his missus and Mary went out to Plotsky's farm in the country. In a field by the river a little platform had been built. It was fixed up pretty like the Fourth of July, with flags and red, white and blue paper. Next to it stood a long table with prune-jack, the two barrels of beer, cakes, and pots of polnena kapusta. On the other side of the platform was the gypsy band from Braddock, playing fiddles. Nice sun was shining, and the people were walking around feeling good.

Steve said hello to everybody. He was all dressed up—Sunday suit, hat, necktie, everything. He kept looking at Mary, sitting next to Steve's missus. She was wearing a green and red silk dress, and she was pretty as anything.

Steve was one mighty proud feller. He winked one eye, pulled his mustache, and snapped his red suspenders.

"Hey, Eli," he said, "you feel strong today? Ho, Pete, better you have plenty steam for that contest! Say, Andy, how is your muscle?"

Along about the middle of the afternoon, Steve walked up on the platform. He told the gypsies to stop playing and held up his hand.

"All right," he said, "now I will make speech about the contest. For a long time all the young fellers want to marry my daughter, prettiest girl anywhere. Each feller say he is best and strongest man, make best hoosband for Mary. By golly, I get sick of all that talk. Now we gone find out who is really the strongest man."

He pointed to three long bars of steel in front of the platform.

"Everybody see those dolly bars from steel mill? First one weighs three hundred and fifty pounds. Second one, five hundred pounds. Third one is from bloomer mill and weighs as much as other two put together."

All the people looked at the dolly bars.

"O.K.," said Steve. "Now all you young fellers try to lift those dolly bars. The strongest and best man will be hoosband for Mary, daughter of me, Steve Mestrovich, best cinderman in steel mill, you betcha."

Everybody cheered while the young fellers stood up and took off their shirts. Most of them could lift up the first dolly bar. But the only ones who could lift up the second dolly bar were Pete Pussick, Eli Stanoski and Andy Dembroski.

"Now you try to lift that big dolly bar," said Steve. "By golly, that is some big hunk steel."

Eli Stanoski was the first to try. He smiled as he bent over and took a good grip on the dolly bar. He pulled and the smile came off his face. He pulled again, puffing just like a steam engine. He pulled and puffed, he puffed and pulled. It was no use. He couldn't move the dolly bar an inch.

Andy Dembroski was the next to try. First he went to the table and had a little drink of prune-jack. Then he bent over and pulled. The dolly bar didn't move. He went back to the table, had another drink of prune-jack, and pulled again. He grunted and groaned, he groaned and grunted. The dolly bar stayed on the ground.

"Come on, Pete," said Steve. "Your turn now."

Pete Pussick nodded his head. He walked all around the dolly bar. He walked around six times, maybe, looking it over. He rubbed a little dirt on his hands. He hitched up his pants. He braced his feet against the ground, bent down, and pulled. No good—he couldn't lift that dolly bar.

Pete Pussick wiped his face with a big handkerchief. Once more he walked around the dolly bar. Once more he braced his feet and bent over. Once more he pulled. This time he pulled so hard that his hands slipped and he fell down on the ground.

Before he could get up again, somebody in the crowd laughed: "Ho! Ho!"

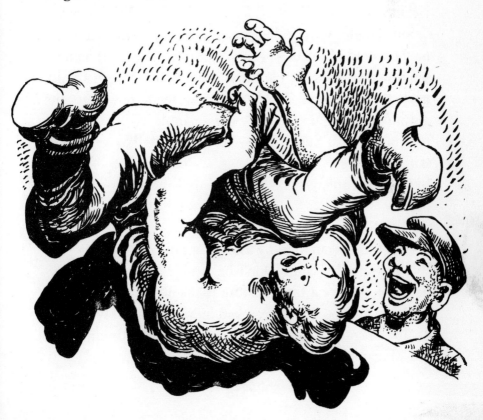

"Who is making laugh at me?" yelled Pete Pussick. "Maybe you think is easy job to lift this dolly bar. You such a strong feller, why don't you lift 'em yourself?"

"O.K.," said a voice, and a feller came walking out of the crowd.

"Looky!" said everybody. "Yoh!"

Because that feller was seven or eight feet tall, about. He was as big around as the smokestack on the steel mill. His back was almost as broad as the gate in the steel mill fence. Oh, he was some man—bigger than Pete Pussick and Eli Stanoski and Andy Dembroski or anybody. He was dressed in Old Country clothes, with a little cap on his head. His pants were too short for him, and so was his jacket.

Still laughing, he rolled up his sleeves. With one hand he took hold of the dolly bar. With the other hand he took hold of Pete Pussick. He lifted them both above his head, gave them a good shake, then put them down on the ground. Picking up the dolly bar again, he twisted it in his two big hands. Sure Mike—he twisted it like a piece of wire.

All the people watched him, their eyes and mouths wide open.

"Yoh!" they said. "Yoh!"

And they began to move away from him.

The big feller said, "Don't be afraid! I'm not hurt anybody. Joost have a little bit fun, that's all."

"Who are you, mister?" asked Steve in a small voice.

"Joe Magarac," answered the man. "That is my name— Joe Magarac."

214

Ho! When the people heard that, they let out one big laugh. Steve shook all over. His missus doubled up laughing. Mary giggled. Pete Pussick laughed so hard he couldn't stand up. Because in the Slovak language magarac means jackass-donkey.

"Oh, my!" said everybody. "That is some name. Joe Magarac—Joe Jackass-Donkey."

Joe Magarac smiled.

"Sure," he said. "Joe Magarac—that is me. I am big and strong and can work like magarac. I was born on ore mountain in Old Country, and I joost come to U.S.A. to work in steel mill. I am only real steel man in world. Looky, I show you."

He pulled off his shirt, and what do you think? He was made of steel all over. He thumped himself on his chest with his big fist. It made a noise like steel—bongk! bongk!

"You are joost the man I was waiting for," said Steve, taking Joe Magarac up on the platform. "You are strongest man anywhere, and you gone be hoosband for my Mary."

216

Making a little bow, Joe Magarac took off his cap to
Mary.

"By golly," he said, "you are prettiest girl I see in all my
life. But I can't be hoosband for you."

"Why not?" asked Steve.

"Joe Magarac got no time to sit around house with
missus," said Joe Magarac. "Joe Magarac work all the time,
make plenty steel. Joost work and eat, that's all. Better for
Mary to marry Pete Pussick. Next to me, he is strongest

man. And I think Mary likes him best of all."

"That is right," said Mary.

Andy Dembroski pushed his way up to the platform.

"Hey, you Steve Mestrovich!" he hollered. "If Joe Magarac is not hoosband for Mary, then you don't have strongest man in world in your fambily. What do you say about that, huh?"

Steve took off his hat and scratched his head.

Then he said, "Joost a minute." Turning to Joe Magarac, he asked, "You maybe got Uncle John in Old Country?"

"No got Uncle John," answered Joe.

"You got maybe Aunt Rosie?"

"No Aunt Rosie."

"You got maybe Uncle Stanley?"

"No. No Uncle Stanley."

"You got Aunt Sophie, maybe?"

Joe Magarac nodded his head. "Aunt Sophie I got."

"Ho!" said Steve. "I got Aunt Sophie in Old Country, too. You are my cousin for sure! That's what I think all the time. So you are in my fambily, even if you don't be Mary's hoosband."

After that Steve didn't waste one little bit of time. He got a priest and an altar boy, and Mary was married to Pete Pussick. Steve gave away the bride and Joe Magarac was best man. Then the gypsies played music and everybody danced. Joe Magarac danced the polka with Mary and with Steve's missus. The people drank prune-jack and beer, and ate cakes and polnena kapusta. Everybody had a big time, you betcha. It wasn't until late at night that they started for home.

Joe Magarac asked Steve where there was a boarding-house in Braddock.

"What for you want boardinghouse?" said Steve. "You are my cousin, you come live with me. Mary will get house of her own with Pete Pussick and we will have plenty room."

"I like that fine," said Joe Magarac. "Because your missus makes the best polnena kapusta I ever taste anyplace."

Steve's missus smiled and said, "You are nice feller, Joe Magarac. I am glad you live with us."

"Sure," said Steve. "You are greenhorn joost like I was when I come from Old Country. But I will get you job in mill, U.S.A. citizen papers, everything."

So Joe Magarac went home with Steve and his missus. When they got to the house, he looked down at the steel mill in the valley. He saw the smoke pouring out of the smokestacks. He saw the red and yellow fire of the furnaces. He heard the noise of the mill and the whistle of trains.

"By golly," he said, "this is fine place! This is fine country! I gone catch U.S.A. citizen papers and be an American. Then I make best steel in world for U.S.A., you betcha your life!"

Early the next morning Steve took Joe Magarac to his foreman at the steel mill. He asked the foreman to give Joe Magarac a job.

"Well, I'll try him out," said the foreman.

Right away Joe Magarac started working on Number 7 open-hearth furnace. First he threw in ore, scrap, limestone —everything to make steel. Then he sat in the furnace door, with the fire coming up around him. As the ore melted, he stirred it with his big hands. While he worked, he sang "Columbia, the Gem of the Ocean." He didn't know all the words, so he sang it this way:

Coloombia, the Jim of the oocean!
Yoh! Hooray for the U.S.A.!

After the ore melted, he scooped up a little steel. He tasted it, blowing the steam out through his nose.

"She's cook up good," he said. "Time to tap 'em out."

Crawling into the furnace, he dumped the steel into ingot molds with his hands. He jumped out, ran to the other end of the mill, and again picked up the steel. He squeezed it through his fingers, making rails. He made eight rails at a time, four with each hand. He made rails faster and better than anybody, you betcha!

"How you like?" Joe Magarac asked the foreman.

"By golly!" said the foreman, over and over again. "By golly!"

"What I tell you?" said Steve proudly. "My cousin Joe Magarac is best steel man in world."

And the other men in the mill said, "That Joe Magarac, he is a magarac for sure."

Come payday, Joe Magarac went with Steve to a clothing store. He got him a Sunday suit, necktie, work pants, work shirts—everything. He couldn't get a hat big enough, but he bought the largest one there was. At the Star Shoe Corner he bought a pair of Size 18 extra-special wide-last triple-soled safety-toe shoes. Then he went to the store next door and bought a washtub. When he got home he fixed it up with a lid and a handle and used it for a lunch bucket. Every day Steve's missus filled it up with polnena kapusta for his lunch.

Joe Magarac had been making steel for two or three weeks, about, when one day a man came walking into the mill. He was dresed up fine, in a Prince Albert coat. He was smoking a big long cigar. Everybody worked harder than ever, because he was the superintendent of the mill. He walked along until he saw Joe Magarac making steel with his hands.

"It can't be," he said. "But it is. Isn't it?"

"Is," said Steve. "That is Joe Magarac, cousin of me, Steve Mestrovich, best cinderman in mill. He is real steel man."

"Sure, Mr. Boss Super," said Joe Magarac. And he thumped himself on the chest—bongk! bongk!

"What kind of man are you? Where are you from?" the super asked.

"Joost come from Old Country," answered Joe Magarac.

"A greenhorn, eh?"

"That is right, Mr. Boss Super. But pretty soon I gone catch U.S.A. citizen papers. Then I will be American like everybody else."

"Citizen papers, eh?" said the super. "You'll have to save up some money first. It will cost you a thousand dollars to become a citizen."

"It only cost me five dollars, Boss Super," said Steve.

The super shook his head.

"That's because you're a small man," he said. "For a big

man it costs more. Big man, big citizen—it cost more. Joe will have to pay about a thousand dollars. Turn out a lot of steel, Joe. Save your money, and by and by you'll have enough to become a citizen."

The super gave a little laugh, blew out smoke rings, and walked away.

"I think maybe Boss Super make joke," said Steve.

"Why should Boss Super make joke with greenhorn like me?" said Joe Magarac. "By golly, I got to get thousand dollars so I can catch U.S.A. citizen papers."

All day Joe Magarac worried about what to do. He worried while he ate polnena kapusta from his washtub. He worried while he cooked steel. He worried while he made rails. But when the quitting-time whistle blew, he smiled.

"Steve," he said, "I got good idea how to make plenty money for U.S.A. citizen papers. I will work day turn *and* night turn, make double money."

"When you gone sleep?" asked Steve.

"Steel man don't need sleep," laughed Joe Magarac. "Joost work and eat. Joe Magarac—that's me."

They hurried over to the foreman and asked him to give Joe Magarac an extra job. And what do you think? The foreman said no. He said he never heard of such a thing. Joe Magarac or no Joe Magarac, nobody could work day and night.

Slowly Joe Magarac and Steve left the mill. They walked up the hill to Steve's house without saying a word. They washed and sat down at the table to eat. Just as Steve's missus was bringing them a pot of polnena kapusta, Steve banged his fist on the table.

He said, "Joe Magarac, I know what you gone do. You go over to Homestead mill, catch job there, too. You don't tell them you have job in Braddock. You work day turn in one place, night turn in the other. You make double money, and you save enough for U.S.A. citizen papers."

Steve's missus folded her arms and gave Steve a look.

"Better you not be such a Smarty Aleck, Mr. Steve Mestrovich," she said. "Maybe Joe Magarac will get into trouble if he works in two mills."

"You think I will get trouble, Steve?" asked Joe Magarac.

Steve leaned back in his chair. He winked one eye, pulled his mustache, and snapped his red suspenders.

"Ho!" he said. "You do what I tell you. Everything gone be O.K."

Joe Magarac ate some polnena kapusta, then took a streetcar to Homestead. He got a job there, and after that he worked day and night. As soon as the quitting-time whistle blew in Homestead, he took a streetcar to Braddock. As soon as the quitting-time whistle blew in Braddock, he took a streetcar to Homestead. He made good steel in both places, and he saved his money to get his U.S.A. citizen papers.

Joe Magarac had been working in Homestead for two or three weeks, about, when one day the superintendent came walking through the mill. Just like the Braddock super, he was dressed up fine in a Prince Albert coat. Just like the Braddock super, he smoked a big cigar. This super didn't like to talk much. He stopped in front of Joe Magarac, looked him up and down, and said, "Hm."

The super watched Joe Magarac throw ore, scrap and

limestone into the furnace. He watched Joe Magarac cook steel, and squeeze out rails with his hands.

"Hm," he said, and walked away.

Now Joe Magarac didn't know it, but that same night the Homestead super visited the Braddock super. They sat in the parlor of the Braddock super's big house, smoking their cigars.

"I hear you're turning out a lot of steel these days," said the Braddock super.

"Hm," said the Homestead super.

"But we're turning out even more at Braddock," said the Braddock super.

"Hm?" said the Homestead super.

"That's because the Braddock steel men are the best and strongest in the world," said the Braddock super.

"Hm!" said the Homestead super.

"That's right," answered the Braddock super. "Why, I've got one man who—"

"Got a better one!" shouted the Homestead super, jumping up.

"I don't know about that."

"I do. Beat your man any day."

"And when will that be?"

"Any time you say!"

"Do you mean that?" asked the Braddock super.

"I do."

"All right," said the Braddock super. "The mills are having a picnic at Kennywood Park this Sunday. Suppose we have a little contest—your man against mine. Then we'll see which one is stronger."

"Hm," said the Homestead super, nodding his head.

The next day both the Homestead super and the Braddock super spoke to Joe Magarac. Each of them said, "Joe, how would you like to be in a little contest at the picnic? I want everybody to see how strong you are."

And Joe Magarac said to each of them, "Sure, Mr. Boss Super. I am strongest man in mill anywhere. I will win that contest for sure."

Come Sunday, Joe Magarac and Steve put on their Sunday suits. Together with Steve's missus and Mary and Pete Pussick, they started out for the picnic. Steve carried a big basket of lunch, while Joe Magarac carried his washtub of polnena kapusta.

They got on the streetcar that was crowded with people going to the picnic. The men all wore their Sunday suits. Their missuses wore white dresses. They all carried baskets of lunch, and they laughed and talked all the way.

At Kennywood Park Joe Magarac had a fine time riding on the merry-go-round and the roller coaster. After eating his polnena kapusta, he went to a big field where there was a grandstand. A band was playing, flags were flying, and the seats were filled with people.

In the front row of the grandstand sat the Braddock super and the Homestead super. Like everybody else, they were watching the men from the two mills run races. Pretty soon, though, some fellers carried in three big dolly bars. They were the same kind Joe Magarac had lifted at Steve's party. The band stopped playing and the Braddock super stood up.

"Folks," he said, "the superintendent of the Homestead mill says that Homestead men are the strongest in the world."

The Homestead people cheered, but the Braddock people went "Ho! Ho!"

The Braddock super said, "I say that the Braddock men are the strongest."

Now the Braddock people cheered, while the Homestead people went "Ho! Ho!"

"Well," said the Braddock super, "we'll see. We're going to have a little contest between the two strongest men in the mills. They'll try to lift those dolly bars, and may the best man win."

He and the Homestead super both looked at Joe Magarac.

"Ready?" they asked.

"Sure Mike," answered Joe Magarac, jumping up.

"Where's your man?" said the Braddock super to the Homestead super.

"Where's yours?" said the Homestead super.

"My man is here."

"So's mine."

"Where?"

"Right there," said the Homestead super, pointing to Joe Magarac.

"Couldn't be," said the Braddock super. "That's my man."

"He's not!" yelled the Homestead super.

"He is!" yelled the Braddock super. Then he turned to Joe Magarac. "Where do you work, Joe?" he asked. "In Braddock?"

"Sure," said Joe Magarac, "in Braddock."

The Homestead super said, "You're sure you don't work in Homestead?"

"Sure," said Joe Magarac. "Work in Homestead."

"Just where *do* you work?" asked the Braddock super. "You can't work in both places at once."

"That's what I do, Mr. Boss Super," said Joe Magarac. "Work in Braddock and Homestead. Work one place day turn, other place night turn. That way I make double money to pay for my U.S.A. citizen papers."

When the people in the grandstand heard that, they began to laugh. They pointed to the supers, laughing and slapping one another on the back. The supers' faces got red. Oh, my, they were angry as anything. They looked around at the people. They looked at each other. Then they looked at Joe Magarac.

"You're fired!" they hollered.

"Joost a minute, Boss Supers!" called Steve. "You don't want to fire Joe Magarac. He is strongest man anywhere."

"We don't, don't we?" said the supers.

"You think it over. Then maybe you won't do it."

"We won't, won't we?"

Before Steve could answer, the supers yelled, "You're fired, too!" And they left the grandstand together.

The band started playing again, but Joe Magarac didn't hear it. The sun was shining, but he didn't see it. He sat down, holding his head in his hands.

"Steve," he said, "you lose your job because of me."

"Don't you worry about that," said Steve. "But how you gone catch thousand dollars for U.S.A. citizen papers?"

People crowded around Steve and Joe Magarac. They said, "You go see Boss Super tomorrow. Maybe you get your job back again."

Steve started to walk up and down like a rooster in a barnyard.

"Why should best man in mill ask for job back?" he said. "Joe, we will go to Scranton and work in coal mine. You will be best miner in world, catch U.S.A. citizen papers, everything. Then the supers gone ask us to come back to steel mill. If we feel like, we go back. If not, not."

Oh, that Steve Mestrovich, he was some proud man!

Joe Magarac asked, "You think that will be best thing?"

Steve's missus folded her arms and gave Steve a look.

"Better you not be such a Smarty Aleck, Mr. Steve Mestrovich," she said.

Steve winked one eye, pulled his mustache, and snapped his red suspenders.

"Ho!" he said. "You do what I tell you. Everything gone be O.K."

Right away hurry-up-quick Steve and Joe Magarac got ready to leave. They said good-by to all the people. They went to Steve's house and packed their clothes. They took one look at the steel mill, then they went to the railroad station and took the train. Steve's missus went with them to make polnena kapusta.

As they rode along, Joe Magarac looked out the window. He could see the rails he had made in the mill. They were shinier than any of the other rails in the railroad track.

By and by they reached Scranton. Joe Magarac and Steve and his missus walked straight from the station to the coal mine. Miners were standing near the shaft, ready to start work. Other miners were coming out of the shaft, their faces covered with coal dust. When they saw Joe Magarac, they said, "Yoh! Looky!"

"Hello, everybody," said Steve. "This is Joe Magarac, cousin of me, Steve Mestrovich, best cinderman in steel mill. He is best man in world for making steel, and he gone be best coal miner, you betcha."

"That is right," said Joe Magarac. "I am real steel man, and I am gone dig plenty coal." And he thumped himself on the chest—bongk! bongk!

"By golly," said the miners. "Whoever heard of a steel man in a coal mine?"

"You hear about it now," said Steve. Turning to the foreman, he asked, "What you say, Boss? You got job for us?"

"Well, I'll try you out," answered the foreman.

Joe Magarac and Steve went to the company store, where they bought picks and shovels and miners' caps. Joe Magarac's cap was too small for him, but it was the biggest he could get. Picking up their picks and shovels, they went down the shaft into the mine.

It was as dark as anything in that mine. It was damp, too. Drops of water dripped down from the roof of the mine, falling on Joe Magarac. But he hardly noticed it. He was too busy mining coal. He kept digging up coal and shoveling it into carts pulled by mules. As he worked, he sang:

Coloombia, the Jim of the oocean!
Yoh! Hooray for the U.S.A.!

The boys driving the donkey cart sang back:

My sweetheart's the mule in the mines,
I drive her without any lines,
On the bumper I stand, with my whip in my hand,
My sweetheart's the mule in the mines.

The first day Joe Magarac worked in the mine, he dug up more coal than all the other miners. The second day he dug up as much as all the other miners. The third day he dug half as much as the other miners. The fourth day he dug as much as one of the other miners. And on the fifth day he dug half as much as any of the other miners.

When he and Steve came out of the mine, the other miners and Steve's missus was waiting for them.

"What's the matter, Joe Magarac?" asked the miners. "How come you mine such a little bit coal?"

"I am steel man," answered Joe Magarac. "Water drops down on me in mine, and it makes me rusty. I get rusty, I can't move my arms so good. That is why I dig only a little bit coal."

"Well," said the foreman, "if you can't mine coal, I'll give you a job driving one of the donkey carts."

The miners began to laugh like anything.

"Joe Magarac gone drive donkey cart like little boy!" they said. "That is good pair—mule and magarac!"

Joe Magarac hung his head.

He said, "That is all I am good for now—to work with mule. And how am I gone catch one thousand dollars for U.S.A. citizen papers?"

"Coal mine is no place for steel man," laughed the miners. "If you want to be miner, maybe you go someplace and mine steel."

"Joost a minute, joost a minute," said Steve. "That is fine idea. Joe, we will go to Minnesoota, work on Mesabi Range and mine iron ore. Then you show these fellers you are best miner anywhere."

"That sound pretty good," said Joe Magarac.

Steve's missus folded her arms and gave Steve a look.

"Better you not be such a Smarty Aleck, Mr. Steve Mestrovich," she said.

Steve winked one eye, pulled his mustache, and snapped his red suspenders.

"Ho!" he said. "You do what I tell you. Everything gone be O.K."

And right away hurry-up-quick Joe Magarac and Steve and his missus started for Minnesota. For a long time they rode on the train, but at last they got there. They went straight from the station to the open-pit mine.

Standing on a little hill, they looked down. In the ground was a big pit of red iron ore. Hundreds of men were in the

233

pit—Finnish fellers, Slovak fellers, all kinds of fellers. Some of them dug up the ore with shovels. Others loaded it into cars that stood on tracks. Engines chugged along the tracks, pulling away the cars full of ore.

"By golly," said Joe Magarac, "that is one big hole for sure."

The miners saw Joe Magarac and ran over to have a good look at him.

"Yoh!" they said.

"He's sizable, all right," said the foreman.

"Sure, Boss," said Joe Magarac.

Steve said, "That is Joe Magarac, cousin of me, Steve Mestrovich, best cinderman in steel mill. He is most sizable man in country. He is real steel man and he is gone show you how to dig that ore."

"We'll soon see about that," said the foreman, handing Joe Magarac a shovel.

Joe Magarac shook his head.

"I don't need any shovel, Boss," he said. "I got better way."

Joe Magarac tossed away the shovel. He rolled up his sleeves and began digging ore with his hands. He dug up the ore and dumped it right into a car standing on the tracks. He was still a little bit rusty, but before long the car was loaded to the top.

All the ore miners let out a cheer.

"That is a magarac for sure," they said.

After that Joe Magarac and Steve mined ore every day. Steve's missus made them plenty of polnena kapusta, which Joe Magarac carried in his washtub.

234

As Joe Magarac dug up the ore, he sang:

Coloombia, the Jim of the oocean!
Yoh! Hooray for the U.S.A.!

The ore miners sang right back:

Perk your ears up, pardner mine,
Cap'n coming down the line,
Scratch the dirt a little more,
Cover up the low-grade ore.

Joe Magarac had been working in the open-pit mine for two or three weeks, about, when one day the foreman came over to him.

"Joe Magarac," said the foreman, "you dig up a lot of that ore. We're going to send the finest ore in the world to the steel mill in Braddock. They're going to make the finest steel in the world, for a new building for Congressmen in Washington, D.C."

"Don't you worry about that, Boss," said Joe Magarac. "I gone dig up plenty fine ore."

And he did just as he said, working faster than ever. Pretty soon, though, the sky became dark. Big, black clouds rolled up, and thunder made a noise—boom! boom! Lightning flashed, and the rain poured down. Oh, my, it rained like anything. All the ore miners put on boots and raincoats and kept on digging. But Joe Magarac just stood there, not doing a thing.

"What's the trouble?" asked the foreman.

"I think I go home, Boss," answered Joe **Magarac**. "If I stay out in the rain, I will get rusty."

"What!" said the foreman. "You going to let a little rain stop you? What kind of ore miner are you, anyway?"

"Joe Magarac is steel man, Boss," said Steve.

"Then let him go back to the steel mill!" yelled the foreman. "Because we've got to get that ore out, no matter how hard it rains!"

"Joe Magarac is like little baby," laughed the other miners. "When rain comes, he has to go home."

Joe Magarac nodded his head sadly and began to run. Steve ran along with him. They reached their house, went in, and sat down at the table. Steve's missus brought them some polnena kapusta, but they couldn't eat.

"What I gone do now?" said Joe Magarac. "If I mine ore in the rain, I will only be good for scrap pile. And if I can't mine ore, how will I get thousand dollars for my U.S.A. citizen papers?"

"By golly," Steve shouted, "I joost get good idea. U.S.A. government needs best steel for that Congressman building. You are best man for making steel anywhere."

"That is right," said Joe Magarac. "But how can I make steel if I am not in steel mill?"

"You listen to me," said Steve. "We will go back to Braddock. At night we will climb the fence, go into the mill, and make that steel. When Boss Super sees that good steel you make, he gone give you back your job, you betcha."

Steve's missus folded her arms and gave Steve a look.

"Better you not be such a Smarty Aleck, Mr. Steve Mestrovich," she said.

Steve winked one eye, pulled his mustache, and snapped his red suspenders.

236

"Ho!" he said. "You do what I tell you. Everything gone be O.K."

And right away hurry-up-quick Joe Magarac and Steve and his missus packed up their clothes. Joe Magarac picked up his washtub, and they set out for Braddock. For a long time they rode on the train, but at last they got there. It was late at night, and Joe Magarac and Steve went straight to the steel mill.

For a while they looked up at the furnaces and the smoke-stacks. They watched the smoke pouring out, and the red and yellow fires.

"By golly!" said Joe Magarac. "This is only place for me. Coal mine is all right for coal miner feller. Ore mine is all right for ore miner feller. But I am steel man, and steel mill is the place for me."

He leaned over, picked up Steve, and lifted him to the top of the fence around the mill. He climbed up himself, jumped down, and helped Steve to get down, too. Together they walked over to Number 7 blast furnace.

"Joe Magarac!" said the men in the mill.

"Hey! What are you doing here?" said the foreman. "You don't have a job in the mill any more!"

"Maybe I don't have job," answered Joe Magarac. "But tonight I'm gone work. I cook you up best steel in world for Congressman building."

Before the foreman could stop him, Joe Magarac began to make steel. First he threw ore, scrap and limestone into the furnace. Then he sat in the furnace door, with the fire coming up around him. As the ore melted, he stirred it with his big hands.

237

The foreman ran to get the super, but Joe Magarac went on making steel. He tasted a little of it, blowing the steam out through his nose.

"She's cook up good," he said. "Time to tap 'em out."

Just then the super came rushing in, yelling and hollering.

"What's going on here?" he shouted.

"Joost a minute, Boss Super," said Steve. "Everything gone be O.K. Joe Magarac, cousin of me, Steve Mestrovich, is making you best steel in world for Congressman building."

All of a sudden they heard a big splash behind them.

"Help!" hollered the men in the mill. "Get the amboolance! Get the doctor! Help!"

"What happened?" asked the super.

"Joe Magarac fall in ladle!" the men answered.

The super looked at the ladle, and what do you think? There was Joe Magarac, with the hot steel boiling up around him.

"Hello, Boss Super," said Joe Magarac. "I am still little bit rusty. I have accident and fall in."

"By golly," said Steve, "you get out or you gone be melted down yourself."

"Too late for me to get out, Steve," said Joe Magarac. "I start to melt already. But that is all right. You roll out this steel with me inside. You make girder with that steel to hold up Congressman building in Washington, D.C. It will be best girder in world, you betcha."

And Joe Magarac just sat back in the hot steel and melted a little more.

"Joe Magarac, you get out of that ladle!" yelled the super.

"Joe!" called Steve. "Hey! Checkai! Stop!"

Joe Magarac smiled and winked one eye. Then the steam hissed, the steel bubbled and boiled, and he was all melted away.

The men stood there, looking at the ladle. Slowly they took off their hats, and Steve wiped a tear from his eye. After a while the super told the men to do as Joe Magarac asked. They poured out the hot steel into ingot molds and rolled it into a girder. It was the best steel ever made, with no seam or pipe or anything. Near one end of the girder two little eyes peeped out. They were so small nobody noticed them.

The girder with Joe Magarac inside was loaded on a flatcar. All the men in the mill watched as the train started for Washington, D.C.

Steve waved his hand and said, "Goom-by, Joe Magarac. You were best steel man anywhere, cousin of me, Steve Mestrovich, best cinderman in mill. And now you are best steel girder in world."

After that the train rolled on to Washington, D.C. The girder was set up near the Capitol. Other girders were attached to it, and brick and marble were piled on. Joe Magarac held it all up. Through a chink in the marble he looked out. He could see the Capitol dome and the tall Washington Monument.

"By golly," he thought, "this is fine place. This is fine country. I am glad I hold up this building for Congressmen."

All through the hot summer and the cold winter Joe Magarac held up the building. He watched Congressmen and Senators coming and going. He saw the President and all kinds of people. When the cold winter was over, Joe Magarac saw the cherry trees bloom. He looked down into the street, and what do you think? There was Steve and his missus.

"Here is Congressman building," Steve was saying. "This is where Joe Magarac is in girder. He was best steel man anywhere, cousin of me, Steve Mestrovich, best cinderman in mill. How you doing, Joe? We make little trip to see Washington, D.C."

Steve winked one eye, pulled his mustache, and snapped his red suspenders. As he and his missus walked away, a Congressman and a Senator came along. They were wearing big hats and shoestring ties.

The Congressman looked at Steve and his missus.

"Foreigners," said the Congressman.

"Too many of them in this country," said the Senator.

"Just what I was thinking, Senator," said the Congressman. "We've got too many foreigners in the U.S.A.—and everybody knows they're no good."

"That's right, Congressman. These Hunkies and Bohunks—they're no good at all."

"I agree, Senator. Slovak fellers, Hungarian fellers, Russian fellers, Irish fellers, Greek fellers, Mexican fellers, Italian fellers—they're just no good."

"And Jewish fellers and colored fellers are the same."

"That's right."

"They're lazy."

"They're dirty."

"They don't talk right."

"They don't look right."

"They've got funny names."

"They've got funny ways."

"They ought to go back where they came from, Congressman."

"That's right, Senator. They're not Americans and never will be. They're not like you."

"Nor like you, Congressman."

"No, I guess we're two of the best Americans that anybody could find. And we'll have to get the foreigners out
of the country."

"That's true, Congressman. There ought to be a law
against 'em. What do you say we think one up?"

"Just what I had in mind, Senator. Then this country
will be fit to live in."

When Joe Magarac heard that, he grew red hot with
anger. He was so hot that he began to boil. As he boiled,

he melted into hot steel. He melted all the way down to the ground, and the wall of the building crashed. Then he began to cool off. But he didn't turn back into a girder. He was Joe Magarac again, standing there in the middle of the bricks and marble, with a cloud of dust around him.

"Look out!" hollered the Congressman.

"Help!" yelled the Senator.

Steve and his missus heard the noise and turned around. "By golly," said Steve, "that is Joe Magarac for sure!"

Joe Magarac roared at the Congressman and the Senator: "That is right! I am Joe Magarac, that is who I am! I was born on ore mountain in Old Country, and I come to America to catch citizen papers and make best steel in U.S.A. I make plenty steel for railroads and I cook myself into girder for Congressman building. Now you say I am Hunky foreigner. You say I am no good and should go back where I came from. O.K. I go back. But if I am not good enough for you, my steel is not good enough either. So I will rip out all the steel rails I ever make. Then I go back to Old Country." And he gave himself a big, big thump on the chest—BONGK! BONGK!

"Joost a minute, Joe," said Steve. "You don't want to leave U.S.A."

"I don't stay in country where they call me names," said Joe Magarac.

With Steve and his missus running after him, Joe Magarac walked down Pennsylvania Avenue. He walked to the railroad station, then out to the railroad tracks. He looked for the rails he had made and ripped them out. He twisted them into knots and tossed them aside.

Trains stopped. Railroad fellers hollered. Steve yelled. Policemen came running up.

"Put down those rails," they said.

Joe Magarac just laughed a big laugh.

"Ho!" he said. "Who gone arrest steel man like me?"

And the policemen all backed away from him.

"By golly," said Steve. "I better do something to stop Joe. He gone broke up the whole country. I think I have good idea."

Steve's missus folded her arms and gave him a look.

"Better you not be such a Smarty Aleck, Mr. Steve Mestrovich," she said. "What you gone do?"

Steve winked one eye, pulled his mustache, and snapped his red suspenders.

"You come along with me," he said. "Everything gone be O.K."

Steve started back toward the Congressmen building. Joe Magarac let him go. He kept ripping up the rails and twisting them into knots. Crowds of people watched him, asking him to stop. Joe Magarac just laughed and said, "I don't stay in country like this! I don't want U.S.A. citizen papers any more! I go back to Old Country and make steel!"

Along about evening, though, soldiers came marching up—tramp! tramp! There were infantry fellers with rifles, artillery fellers with cannons, cavalry fellers on horseback. They spread across the tracks and all around Joe Magarac, surrounding him.

A general on a white horse took out his sword and said, "Joe Magarac, I order you to stop ripping up those rails."

Joe bent down and looked the general in the eye.

"Ho!" he said. "You bring whole U.S.A. Army to stop Joe Magarac. But you can't do that. How you gone shoot steel man? It not hurt me one bit."

Just then he heard Steve's voice.

"Hey! Checkai! Stop!" said Steve.

The soldiers stepped aside, making way for a carriage. In the carriage was Steve and a Congressman.

"This is Boss Congressman," said Steve. "He want talk to you."

Joe Magarac said he didn't want to listen to any more Congressmen. All the same, he did listen.

"Joe Magarac," said the Boss Congressman, "if you want

to rip up rails, I can't stop you. If you want to go back to the Old Country, I can't stop you. But before you do anything, I wish you would come with me."

"Where you gone take me?" asked Joe Magarac.

"You'll see," said Steve. "You come along, Joe. You will find out something."

"Well, all right," said Joe Magarac, getting into the carriage. They drove to the Capitol Building, went inside—and what do you think? All the Congressmen and Senators were there.

The Boss Congressman stood up before them and made a speech. He said that anybody who didn't want Joe Magarac to stay in the U.S.A. didn't know anything. He said that the Indians were the only people in the U.S.A. who didn't come from someplace else. He said that the whole U.S.A. was built up by people from the Old Country, and that the U.S.A. needed Joe Magarac to make steel. He said that anybody who helped build up the U.S.A. wasn't a foreigner any more. And he said that nobody was better than anybody else, no matter where he came from.

By golly, when he finished his speech some of those Congressmen and Senators looked mighty ashamed. Two or three of them even sneaked out of the room. Then the Boss Congressman asked everybody to vote on whether Joe Magarac should stay in the U.S.A.

"Aye!" voted the Congressmen and the Senators.

"I move we make Joe Magarac a citizen," said the Boss Congressman.

"Second the motion! Aye!" said the Congressmen and Senators.

250

The Boss Congressman turned to Joe Magarac and said, "Well, Joe Magarac, you can leave if you want to. If you want to go back to the Old Country we can't stop you. But the U.S.A. Congress asks you to stay and be an American."

"I don't know," answered Joe Magarac, scratching his head. "Where am I gone catch thousand dollars for citizen papers?"

"Ho!" laughed Steve. "You don't need thousand dollars, Joe. Boss Super in mill only make joke because you are greenhorn."

"That's right," said the Boss Congressman. "It wasn't a very nice joke—but that's all it was."

Joe Magarac looked at Steve. He looked at the Boss Congressman. He looked around at all the Congressmen and Senators, and then he smiled.

"O.K.," he said. "I stay."

"Hooray!" yelled the Congressmen and the Senators. They crowded around him and took him to the White House, where the President of the U.S.A. was waiting.

"Come in, Joe Magarac," the President said.

He shook hands with Joe Magarac and gave him his U.S.A. citizen papers. Then they sat back and ate polnena kapusta that Steve's missus had made in the White House kitchen. A band played, and Joe Magarac danced the polka

with the President's missus. When the party was over, he
went back to Braddock.

The super of the mill said he was sorry he had played a joke on Joe Magarac. He opened the gates of the mill and people from everywhere came in to watch Joe Magarac work on Number 7 open-hearth furnace. They watched as he put in ore, scrap, limestone—everything to make steel. They watched as he stirred the steel with his hands and tasted it.

"She's cook up fine," said Joe Magarac. "Time to tap 'em out."

He poured the steel into ingot molds and squeezed out rails with his hands. Everybody cheered, and Steve was as proud as anything.

"Yoh!" he said. "That is Joe Magarac, U.S.A. citizen, best man for to make steel in world, cousin of me, Steve Mestrovich, best cinderman in mill, by golly!"

Steve's missus folded her arms and gave him a look.

"Better you not be such a Smarty Aleck, Mr. Steve Mestrovich," she said.

Steve winked one eye, pulled his mustache, and snapped his red suspenders. Joe Magarac thumped himself on the chest—bongk! bongk!

"Ho!" they said together. "You do what I tell you. Everything gone be O.K."

And that is how Joe Magarac got his U.S.A. citizen papers. And after that, he **made plenty** steel for the U.S.A. You betcha your life!

The Developing Child

Recent decades have witnessed unprecedented advances in research on human development. Each book in The Developing Child series reflects the importance of this research as a resource for enhancing children's well-being. It is the purpose of the series to make this resource available to that increasingly large number of people who are responsible for raising a new generation. We hope that these books will provide rich and useful information for parents, educators, child-care professionals, students of developmental psychology, and all others concerned with childhood.

Jerome Bruner, University of Oxford
Michael Cole, Rockefeller University
Barbara Lloyd, University of Sussex
Series Editors

The
Psychology of
Childbirth

Aidan Macfarlane

Harvard University Press
Cambridge, Massachusetts
1977

Library of Congress Cataloging in Publication Data
Macfarlane, Aidan, 1939-
    The psychology of childbirth.
    (The Developing child)
    Bibliography: p.
    Includes index.
    1. Childbirth—Psychological aspects.
2. Infant psychology. 3. Mother and child.
I. Title [DNLM: 1. Labor. 2. Maternal
behavior. 3. Prenatal care. 4. Parent—Child
relations. 5. Child development. WQ200 M143p]
RG658.M3   155.4'22   76-51311
ISBN 0-674-72105-5 (cloth)
ISBN 0-674-72106-3 (paper)

This book is dedicated to Elizabeth, Magnus, and Tamara.

Contents

The
Developing
Child

The
Psychology of
Childbirth

Prologue

The complex social and behavioral changes within our society frequently seem to defeat the analytic endeavors of psychologists, sociologists, economists, and philosophers. It is, however, fortunate that the world is also populated with those who are unable to accept the limitations of science and scientific methods, people for whom the inability to quantify emotion, mysticism, and change still provides a certain joy and satisfaction.

One of the recent major social changes for which it is difficult to assign causes has been the reassessment of the position of women within our society and of their role in childbearing. From the standpoint of medical management, childbirth has been mainly a male prerogative, with the result that the physical aspects of birth have been better managed than the emotional ones. It would be difficult to deny the enormous benefits in terms of decrease in death and damage to babies and mothers which medical advances have brought about. Therefore I frequently emphasize in this book that it is only possible to examine the psychological aspects of childbirth in the knowledge that both mother and baby have an optimal chance of survival.

The reduction of the deathrate among mothers and their babies, however, has meant more and more interference in the processes of birth. Mothers now having babies are considered "patients in hospitals" rather than human beings who go through normal physiological and psychological developments. To a certain extent we seem to have reached a point of diminishing returns: increasing interference provides less and less in terms of improved outcome. In spite of lip service paid to the idea that psychological and physiological changes are so linked that

1

changes in one area do not occur without changes in the other, little use is made of the connection. Nevertheless, psychological factors can be used both to predict where trouble may occur in pregnancy and birth and to improve the quality of the experience.

Childbirth is an emotional and immeasurably complex aspect of existence, and the experience means a great deal to the individuals involved, both at the time itself and later. Thus recent research into psychology and human behavior can give insights that do not detract from the mystery of birth and increase our knowledge of the exciting possibilities of variation and influence. Nothing in this book is meant to indicate that there is a right or wrong way in childbirth. I simply want to examine some of the recent research findings in an area that may be of interest to those having babies or those helping in the processes of childbirth. None of this information is infallible. The psychology of childbirth is itself still in its infancy and faces extraordinarily difficult methodological problems in disentangling the many possible causes and effects involved in pregnancy and delivery. Thus the information that has been gained should be approached carefully—and it can be accepted or rejected as it seems to respond to the individual's own sensibilities, knowledge, and experience. In some cases it may provide a degree of insight, and in others it may meet with outright rejection.

Although my book is concerned with childbirth, birth is of course only one part of a continually unfolding relationship from conception onward, first between the baby and the mother and, after birth, between the child, the mother, the father, and the environment in general. Because of this, the chapters are chronologically ordered, dealing first with the baby's experiences in the uterus and with the mother's psychology during pregnancy. After these come the delivery and the parents' first reactions to the newborn baby. We move then to the way in which the baby perceives the outside world and how he may influence and be influenced by his new environment.

Between chapters are transcripts of actual deliveries. I video-recorded them in the labor room, as part of a research project on the first meetings of mothers and their babies. Many of the questions raised in this book are related to one question: Does deliv-

ery have any long-term effect? Still it must be emphasized that we do not spend our whole lives worrying about the long-term effects of what we are doing. Rather we are more often concerned with the immediate quality and satisfaction of the experience. This must surely apply to childbirth.

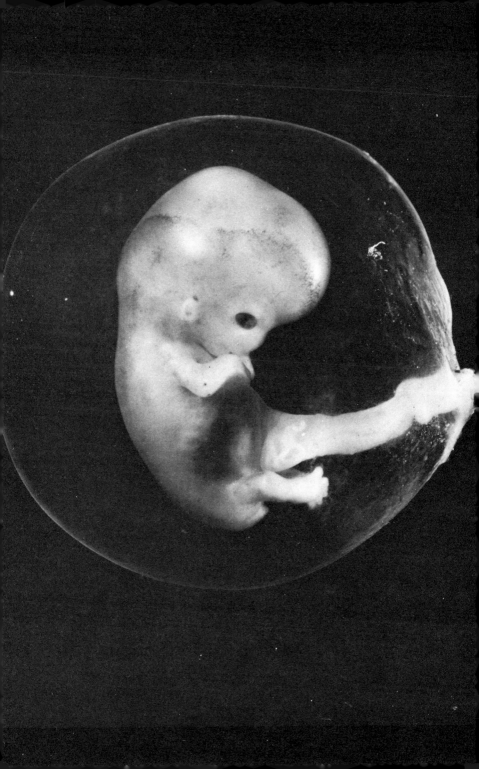

1 / Life Before Birth

It seems extraordinary that astrologers base a horoscope containing predictions for a whole lifetime on the exact time and date of delivery—a time and date that today are more frequently chosen by the obstetrician than by fate.

In China and Japan, a child is considered to be one year old at birth; the child's individual existence during his* development within the mother's uterus is thereby acknowledged from the moment of conception. The importance of this period was well noted by physician and philosopher Sir Thomas Browne, who in 1642 wrote: "Every man is some months older than he bethinks him, for we live, move, have being, and are subject to the actions of the elements and the malice of diseases, in that other world, the truest Microcosm, the womb of our mother." To this the poet Samuel Taylor Coleridge added in 1802, in the margin of Browne's book, "Yes—the history of man for the nine months preceding his birth would probably be far more interesting and contain events of greater moment, than all the three score and ten years that follow it."

The belief that events can influence the unborn child—and may be caused by such factors as magic, the gods, and the planets, or by the infant's own actions, or by events affecting the pregnant woman—has been held through all of recorded history in all cultures. In fact, even today Lyall Watson in *Supernature* gives a very plausible argument for the influence of the planets on human development.[1] Hippocrates in 400 B.C. and Serenus in

*Assuming that the baby is male has no special significance, but it helps avoid confusion with his (or her) mother.

5

the first century A.D. expressed a firm belief that the pregnant woman influenced her unborn child, and a thousand years ago the Chinese were running prenatal clinics, not so much in the interest of physical well-being as to ensure tranquility in the mother and, through her, in the baby. In the Middle Ages, however, magic and demons were believed to hold sway, and midwives were thought to be witches.

Philosophies changed, and by the fifteenth century Leonardo da Vinci could see direct links once more between mother and child: "The things desired by the mother are often found impressed on parts of the child who the mother carried at the time of the desire. So it is concluded that one and the same soul governs the two bodies, and the same body nourishes both." Also current at this time was the agreeable notion that the mother's and father's "imaginings" at conception would influence the outcome of the pregnancy. Since it is possible to assume that on the whole sexual intercourse is a pleasant experience, then most of the outcomes should be good.

The body of scientific opinion during the last century and the earlier part of this one promoted the idea of the uterus as a fortress, impregnable to anything other than sperm. The uterus was imaged as a kind of mausoleum entombing the fetus within it. There was no internal or external stimulation of any kind until, at the end of nine months, life suddenly burst out.

But, as early as 1889, Hirsh had drawn up an impressive list of substances moving from the blood of the mother to the blood of the child across the placental barrier—including opiates, tobacco, and ether; and L. W. Sontag in the 1930s showed how smoking and loud noises could affect the heartrate of a baby in the uterus.[2] The full significance of the interaction between mother and fetus was finally realized at the time of the thalidomide disaster of the 1960s. There are now over 1500 substances that are known to have an adverse effect on the developing fetus. Many of these are drugs, which can cross the placenta rapidly from mother to child. These drugs may have a beneficial effect on the mother (also a deleterious one), but often they have disastrous effects on the embryo. Maternal malnutrition, X-rays, and smoking are among other harmful factors. Mothers who smoke have an increased chance of producing a small or sick baby, and more directly it has been shown that when a pregnant

woman smokes the breathing movements of the fetus are modified for up to an hour after the cigarette.

In its turn, the fetus has an effect on the mother's physiology, as so nicely summed up by Frank Hytten: "The fetus is an egoist, and by no means an endearing and helpless little dependent as his mother may fondly think. As soon as he has plugged himself into the uterine wall he sets out to make certain that his needs are served, regardless of any inconvenience he may cause. He does this by almost completely altering the mother's physiology, usually by fiddling with her control mechanisms."[3]

We all live in a constantly changing world, and we ourselves have to change and adapt to our environment, as well as change and adapt the environment. The internal changes that occur within us are of many different kinds, chemical, mechanical, physiological, psychological. The baby, a single cell at conception, goes through all the inconceivably complex developments to become, at nine months of age in the uterus, as sophisticated as most animals ever are in a lifetime. He has been surrounded by the changing world of his mother's body, which he himself has also been influencing by his own existence. What can we find out about what the world is like to a baby inside his mother?

SOUND IN THE UTERUS

A baby cannot voice his feelings while in the uterus or later remember them to tell us what they were like. Nor can we directly observe his behavior there. We can only use what mothers tell us about their babies' behavior, make inferences by observing babies born long before they have reached full term, or use highly sophisticated equipment like the ultrasonic scanner.

So we must try to derive a good deal about the baby's behavior in the uterus from relatively few observed facts. For instance, if we put a loudspeaker on the tummy of a pregnant mother and play five seconds of, say, Elvis Presley turned up to almost deafening loudness, we would probably notice, if the mother is getting on toward the end of pregnancy, that each time the sound is turned on, the baby becomes more active. But the baby's reaction might depend on how quickly the music is turned up, how loud it gets, what vibration frequencies are being used, how long the sound lasts, or all of these. One can certainly say there is

something about that particular noise that makes the baby more active, though of course we can say nothing about how he "feels" about the sound.

Ever-observant mothers have long been aware that, when they attend a concert or a pop festival, or simply find themselves standing near a door when it slams or near a passing train, their babies tend to become more active in the uterus. In fact, many mothers attribute later sensitivity to sound after birth to such occurrences. The first experimental work done on the effect of sounds and vibrations on the unborn child was carried out by Sontag.[4] In the 1930s he applied a vibrator, producing 120 vibrations a second, to the tummies of eight pregnant women during the last three months of pregnancy and found a marked increase in the babies' movements each time the vibrator was turned on, as well as a marked increase in the babies' heartrate.

It was not clear from this whether the baby was reacting directly to the sound across the tummy wall of the mother or whether his reaction came as a result of the mother herself feeling or hearing the sound. If she suddenly heard a startling sound, she would become more alert, causing a change in the amount of certain hormones excreted in her body; this might in turn contract her uterus slightly, increasing the pressure in the fluid around the baby and making him move. The question was decided by transmitting high-frequency sounds through a vibrator attached to the mother's tummy wall while, at the same time, having her wear headphones into which another sound was played continuously. The high-frequency sounds played for the infant could not be felt or heard by the mother. This method revealed that the babies were indeed reacting directly to the sound and vibration and also that this reaction occurred within five seconds of the sound's being turned on.[5] It also showed that babies responded to low frequencies—so low that they cannot be appreciated by the human ear—which must have been acting at some point on the babies' bodies. There is evidence that sounds the mother hears with her own ears will alter the baby's heartbeat, although not until much more time has elapsed than the five seconds noted when the baby was stimulated directly across the tummy wall.

But what happens to the sound as it passes across the mother's body and through the fluid that surrounds the baby? To answer this question, researchers inserted very small microphones

through the cervix into the uterus to lie alongside the baby's head and record the sounds that come in from the outside.[6] Recordings from these microphones showed, much to everyone's surprise, that there is a very loud noise going on all the time in the uterus. It is a rhythmical whooshing sound, punctuated by the tummy rumbles of air passing through the mother's stomach. The pulsating noise keeps exact time with her heart and is due to blood flowing through her uterus. It turns out that almost all external noises are muted as they pass across the mother's body and through the amniotic fluid, and only extremely loud noises ever exceed the rhythmical sound the baby hears all the time.

The fact that babies are exposed to this sound in the uterus is not without its own significance, for even after birth they do seem to carry some kind of memory of life inside the uterus. Lee Salk noticed that mothers tend to hold their babies on the left side rather than the right (whether they were left- or right-handed), and he noted that most classical paintings of mother and child also show the infant on the left.[7] He proposed that this is because, when held on the left, the head of the baby is close to the mother's heart and that the sound of the heartbeat is comforting. He therefore looked at two groups of a hundred normal babies after birth. To one group he played a recording of an adult heartbeat of 80 beats a minute for four days. The other group had no heartbeat sound. At the end of the four days the heartbeat group had gained more weight and cried significantly less than the other group. Salk also played heartbeats at 120 beats a minute to a third group of babies, but they became so upset that he immediately had to stop the sound. More recently some Japanese pediatricians extended Salk's techniques by making a recording of the noise in the uterus and playing it to babies aged from birth to fourteen days. This sound had a marked calming effect, though I cannot help believing that it must be infinitely nicer being cuddled by mother than lying in a plastic crib listening to a recording of an anonymous uterus.

MOVEMENTS IN THE UTERUS

A baby makes several different kinds of movements in the uterus. First there are those in response to having some part of his body touched. Second there are those he makes spontane-

ously. Last there are movements of the chest, which seem to be breathing.

Movements in response to touch have mainly been observed in babies born very prematurely. But self-stimulation also occurs in the uterus: the baby is capable of touching parts of his body with his hands or feet, and the umbilical cord must also come into contact with his body and limbs. He makes many so-called reflexive movements: some away from the "touch," as if he were programmed to avoid it as harmful. Later in development these reflexes may become reversed, as if he were seeking to explore the touch.

At six weeks after conception the baby is about 2.5 centimeters long (almost one inch), and at this time his hands are held close to the mouth. If the hands touch the area around his mouth, he turns his head away and opens his mouth. Later, instead of turning away from the hand, he turns his head toward it and may even put a finger into his mouth. (Finger sucking is well known to occur in the uterus.) This turning also occurs after the baby has been born, and is called the rooting reflex.

At nine weeks after conception the baby's hand is well enough formed so that, if the palm of the hand is touched, he will bend his fingers; at twelve weeks the fingers and thumb will close. Pressure at the base of his thumb will also cause him to open his mouth and move his tongue. By twenty-five weeks the baby's grasp is strong enough to support the weight of his body.

At nine weeks a touch on the sole of the foot makes the baby curl his toes or straighten them out in a fan, as he bends his leg at the knee and hip to remove the foot from the touch. Walking and crawling motions also develop as a response to various positionings the baby finds himself in, and it is thought that these reflexes may enable him to get into the right position to be born.

At eleven weeks the baby is able to swallow, and a cycle of circulation is set up as he swallows some of the surrounding amniotic fluid and then pees it back out.

Mouth movements also show that the baby has the means to produce many sophisticated facial expressions, such as smiles and laughs. Smiles have been noted in babies born thirty-three weeks after conception, and even smaller fetuses have been seen to look pleased or distressed. But we still don't know whether at this stage these expressions accompany actual emotions.

A baby certainly makes spontaneous movements by seven weeks of intrauterine life, but most mothers will not feel their babies moving until between sixteen and twenty-six weeks. (Mothers are very good at telling when their babies are moving, for even when one uses electronic equipment to measure movements, the mother is almost as accurate.) Separate types of movements have been identified. There are slow, squirming movements, which increase during the course of pregnancy. Then there are sharp kicks, increasing in frequency up to the seventh month and then decreasing. Last there are small rhythmic hiccough-like movements, which occur at a low constant rate from the fifth to the ninth month of pregnancy. The amount of each activity varies enormously from one baby to another. Some of the movements follow cyclical variations that may be associated with the different states of sleep the baby goes through in the uterus. These states seem to coincide with the mother's sleep patterns; before birth they appear to be hormonally controlled, but the matching continues even after delivery.

I have already described how the baby may be affected by loud noises. Sontag recorded fetal movement in a group of mothers over several months and showed that the babies' activity increased when the mothers were under emotional stress.[8] If the emotion was intense but brief, there was only a transitory increase in activity, but with emotional upsets that lasted for longer periods of time there was a prolonged increase, up to ten times the normal level. The mothers also reported feeling increased movements when they themselves felt particularly tired.

A baby also makes breathing movements toward the end of pregnancy. Since at this stage he is surrounded by fluid, these are obviously not absolutely comparable to breathing after birth. Reports of these movements have been made by mothers for many years, and some have even noticed rhythmical movements of their own tummy wall! The breathing occurs about 70 percent of the time and may be punctuated by sighing or hiccoughing. It is still debatable whether some of the movements of the baby's chest represent his attempts to cry.

So we know that babies in the uterus are capable both of responding to touch and of producing spontaneous movement.

We cannot yet tell, though, how much of this movement is necessary for normal muscle development, or how much the fetus is learning about his own actions as he kicks his way around the uterus.

SEEING IN THE UTERUS

The muscles for moving the eye and the actual system for seeing develop very early on in pregnancy, and in the uterus the baby makes eye movements both in response to his changing positions and—as he will throughout life—during dreaming sleep. Not surprisingly, very little is actually known about what or how much the fetus sees. There is some evidence that toward the end of pregnancy the uterus and the mother's tummy wall get so stretched that some light does get through to become diffused in the amniotic fluid; it would look like the glow we see through a hand held over the end of a flashlight. If this is so, then the baby may go through periods of light and dark corresponding to the degree of light the mother is exposed to.

Babies born seven months after conception, when given a test with a single flash of light, do show changes in their brain-wave patterns, and at about this time their pupils begin to react to light. Babies can also be quieted with a repeatedly flashing light, at about 80 flashes a minute, even though they have had no previous experience of it—thus they seem to be born with a sensitivity to light rhythms.

The baby in the uterus lives in a warm, noisy, and maybe pink-tinted world, cushioned by surrounding fluid. He is mobile enough to turn somersaults and suck his finger should he so desire (if desire is a word one can use of a baby at this stage). The fluid will, from time to time, give him a gentle squeeze as the uterus contracts. Many influences are at work within this small world. The external environment—be it the far-distant planets or the more immediate social, cultural, and physical environment of the mother—plays a part, directly or through the

mother. And the baby himself generates changes, as he moves, swallows, pees, and touches. With all of this, however, he is also always developing so that he can organize and respond to a very much more social world than he has ever experienced within the uterus.

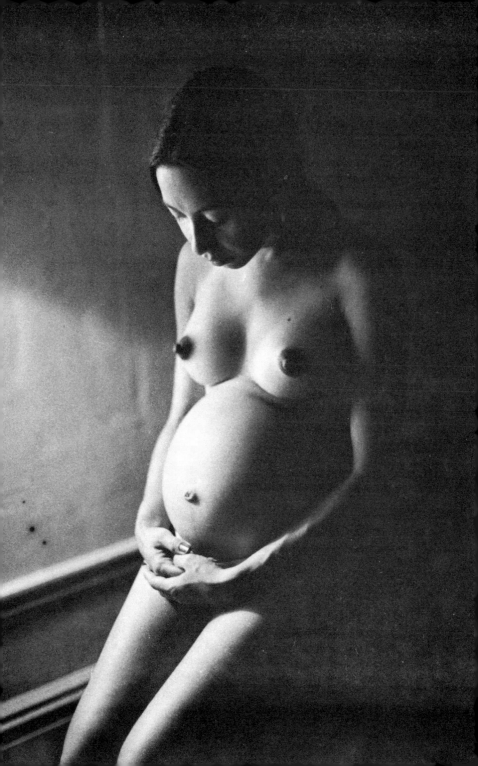

2/ Social and Psychological Factors

In the physical sense there are only two ways of having a baby, vaginally or by cesarean section, but beyond this each and every birth is as individual as the woman herself who gives birth. There are no rights and wrongs, just differences, and in this chapter I want to outline some of the studies that have been made to explain the differences.

Influences on the outcome of a pregnancy and delivery begin at the time of the mother's own conception. The genes she inherits from her parents, her own development inside the uterus with all its complex changes, the hazards of her own delivery, her social and biological experiences during infancy, childhood, and adolescence—all form the basis for her mental and physical health as an adult. There are many other factors as well, such as where she lives, the people she grows up with, her social and economic status. All these affect, among other things, her experience of giving birth and bringing up her own children.

Most of the studies mentioned here have been carried out in Great Britain and the United States, and it is interesting in passing to speculate why certain cultures put emphasis on certain aspects of psychological research rather than on others (for instance, there is a great deal of interest in England on the influence of social-class differences). And a warning is needed here: because of the ever-changing intricacy of human nature, psychological studies on the same subject often fail to get the same results. This is in no way surprising, since it is impossible to ensure that all those people taking part in the study are exactly alike except with respect to the factor under study. It might help research if one could use a single mold to turn out a few thou-

d exact replicas of human beings, and then look at the effect
childbirth of, say, giving half of them a standardized lousy
arriage. However, thanks to God or evolution, we are each
and every one of us at least a little different from the next.

SOCIAL CLASS

Using the concept of social class to categorize portions of a
population according to occupation began around 1910. It was
expedient but perhaps unfortunate that it was the policy then to
put women into different social classes according to their husbands' occupation, even if they had occupations of their own.
To a large extent this method continues today.

The usual method of classification defines five different classes
by occupation: professional; intermediate (for instance, teach-
ers and managers); skilled, manual, or nonmanual; partly
skilled; and unskilled.[1] Now social class is an abstract term—it
only tells you what category someone's occupation puts him in,
and nothing about what particular circumstance (say poor nutrition or heavy smoking) might make a difference because it is a
class difference. As a research tool it has been likened to a doctor's thermometer, which can indicate that a problem exists but
not actually what the problem is.

In England and Wales in 1911, it was decided to see how many
children born to people in each of these five different class-occu-
pations died in the first month of life. The results showed that,
the lower your class, the greater the chance that your baby
would die. In those days the deathrate for babies and mothers
was high, whereas today, after great medical advances, only
about 17 babies in every 1000 dies in the period around birth.
Nevertheless, the same relationship between classes exists: more
babies born to lower-class families die than those born to upper-
class families. This is a strong indication that it is not just better
and more accessible medical care that makes the difference.
What is determined by belonging to a certain social class? Probably what you eat, where you live, how much attention you pay
to your health, and much more. Differences in class seem to be
related to significant differences in the birthweight too, and also
in the incidence of congenital abnormalities. Social class is even
the best predictor of a child's mental and physical development

by the age of twelve. But research has only begun to explore these questions.

Other social factors that seem to affect biological and psychological outcomes include illegitimacy and prenuptial conception, the mother's age, the number of her previous children, her health and physique, and her work during pregnancy. Also important are smoking and drugs, stress and shock, the use of obstetric services, maternal nutrition, and so on. The very incidence of many of these factors as well may be significantly different from class to class.

THE PSYCHOLOGY OF THE MOTHER

A large number of psychological tests have been devised to assess certain variables in a woman's attitudes toward pregnancy. These include her concept of herself as a mother, her general psychosocial adjustment, her mental stability and familial-social adjustment, her notions of femininity. It has been the practice in psychology to try to relate such factors both to upsets in reproductive processes and also to variations within the norm.

Abnormalities of pregnancy and delivery. Habitual spontaneous abortion (miscarriage) has been the subject of extensive psychological research.[2] Tests given to women who have a history of abortion generally differentiate between those with physical diseases that cause the abortions and those without. In one study, both these groups scored quite differently from a control group in which there was no history of aborting. But another study reported that women who habitually aborted were confused over their sexual identity and lacking in support from their social environment. In two other studies, it was found that the cure rate in preventing further spontaneous abortion, by means of psychotherapy, was around 80 percent as compared with a cure rate of 26 percent in a group of aborters not so treated.

Nausea and vomiting would seem to be obvious candidates for psychoanalytic interpretation as disgust or rejection of the pregnancy. There is evidence, however, that the biochemical changes taking place at the beginning of a normal pregnancy do in fact lower a woman's threshold to nausea and vomiting. A

study by S. Rosen, in which he interviewed fifty-four women in the first twelve weeks of pregnancy to assess emotional stress, found that heavy stress was present in all of the eighteen women with severe vomiting; where the amount of vomiting differed with subsequent pregnancies, this too could be correlated with the amount of stress in each of the pregnancies.[3] In yet another study, no relationship was found between vomiting during pregnancy and neurotic symptoms, sexual functioning, attitudes toward pregnancy, emotionally disturbing events, or an extroversion score. To date, then, there has been no conclusive evidence that vomiting during pregnancy is influenced by emotional factors.

The studies on prematurity are unfortunately mainly retrospective—that is, the psychological tests were done after the baby had been born.[4] Therefore, though the tests do show differences between the mothers of full-term babies and those of premature babies, these differences may be the result of having a small and vulnerable baby and have little to do with the reasons why the baby was born prematurely. The role of psychological factors in bringing about premature labor is still uncertain.

Toxemia during pregnancy, marked by hypertension and swelling, has been one of the hardest medical problems to solve. There is an apparent link between high blood pressure and anxiety and stress in people of all conditions, and so toxemia may have a psychosomatic basis. This is not immediately borne out by research, although there is a study by A. Coppen in which he looked at fifty women with toxemia and fifty without. He found significant differences in the two groups in their attitude toward pregnancy and the onset of menstruation; in premenstrual tension; in sexual adjustment; in incidence of vomiting; neuroticism; relation to siblings; and in emotionally disturbing events experienced during pregnancy.[5] Other studies have not uncovered such connections.

There seems to be a relation between anxiety, overt or covert, and the length of labor. Uterine dysfunction may also be associated with concealed anxiety. Harry Bakow found that mothers who were anxious during pregnancy and who expressed more concern over the course of their pregnancy more often had babies who got into distress at delivery.[6] Various more recent studies suggest that women likely to have complications during

childbirth are those who during pregnancy manifested a negative attitude to the pregnancy, showed concern for the condition of the child, saw their employment as being disrupted, listed a greater number of contacts with women who had complicated pregnancies, and described their own mother's health as poor.

These, then, are the results of a few of the studies, but we can see how conflicting they are. Still, the value of all this research is that obstetrics as a whole greatly benefits by any method available that can predict which mothers will have trouble during pregnancy and delivery and which will not. If he has a good method of prediction, an obstetrician can concentrate his energies on the problem mothers and allow the others to deliver without interference, perhaps even at home. It may be that psychological testing in combination with routine medical tests will ultimately improve predictability.

Variations in normal pregnancy and delivery. Psychoanalysis has interpreted the role of normal pregnancy in the life of women in two ways. One interpretation is based on the idea of pregnancy as a crisis, an abnormal state of health which only returns to normal sometime after delivery. The alternative view is that pregnancy and delivery are part of the fuller normal development of a woman.

In support of the former theory, a number of researchers have produced evidence that indicates increased neuroticism in pregnant women. A study by P. A. Chapple and W. D. Furneaux tested women twice during pregnancy, on an introversion-extroversion scale and on a neuroticism scale.[7] They found that as pregnancy progressed the introverted women tended to become more neurotic, the extroverted women less neurotic. Pregnancy, they concluded, acts as a nonspecific stress and the response of women varies according to their personalities.

The view of the birth of a child as a normal stage in female development is well presented by Dana Breene in *The Birth of a First Child.*[8] She set out to test the idea that the biological and psychological event of becoming a mother activates processes that can be "adaptive or maladaptive." She intensively studied fifty women having first babies, using questionnaires, interviews and data collected from obstetricians, as well as formal psychological testing. The results, as one might expect from a

study of this kind, were complex, but she holds that "those women who are most adjusted to childbearing are those who are less enslaved by the experience, have more differentiated, more open appraisals of themselves and other people, do not aspire to be the perfect selfless mother which they might have felt their own mother had not been, but are able to call on a good mother image with which they can identify, and do not experience themselves as passive, the cultural stereotype of femininity."

Emotions and the baby's behavior. As we have seen, there is evidence that the mother's emotions during pregnancy may influence the behavior of the child both in the uterus and after birth. Bakow's work showed that infants who were more alert in their responses when tested after birth tended to have mothers who were well educated and in a high socioeconomic class; babies who were less alert tended to have mothers from less supportive settings who had been more anxious during pregnancy. Further observation revealed a relationship between emotional stress during pregnancy and general restlessness in newborn infants. A. J. Ferreira, who has probably done the most work in this field, gave mothers, thirty-six weeks pregnant, an attitude questionnaire, and he later observed the behavior of their babies in the hospital nursery.[9] He found a correlation between the mother's emotions during pregnancy and the baby's behavior. Another study related a mother's anxiety in pregnancy to her newborn baby's crying: babies of highly anxious mothers cried more, particularly before feeding. The researchers felt that the differences must be due to prenatal or genetic factors rather than to differences in the mother's handling, because the variations in crying between babies of anxious and nonanxious mothers was more marked just before the mothers picked them up for feeding, and because the variations were found as early as the first four days of life. Sontag had already noticed a similar relationship back in 1941 when he looked at the infants of mothers who had experienced prolonged periods of severe anxiety during late pregnancy: these babies too were highly active and intolerant of delays in feeding.[10]

But it has become clear that babies are acutely sensitive to their surroundings and to the characteristics of their caregivers, even immediately after birth. Because of this, it is still an open

question how much the baby's behavior is already influenced by the mother's handling even after only a day of being together. The only way of surely checking whether a baby's behavior stems from prenatal factors is to observe the baby before he has had any postnatal contact with the mother at all.

In some of the studies I have done of young infants, I feel I can pretty much tell in advance which babies will stay awake and not cry during the tests simply by talking to the mothers beforehand. This might be because the mother has in some way, pre- or postnatally, influenced the child's behavior, and I can recognize it from her anxiety; or it might be that she is making me so anxious that, when I handle the baby, I do it badly and the baby cries.

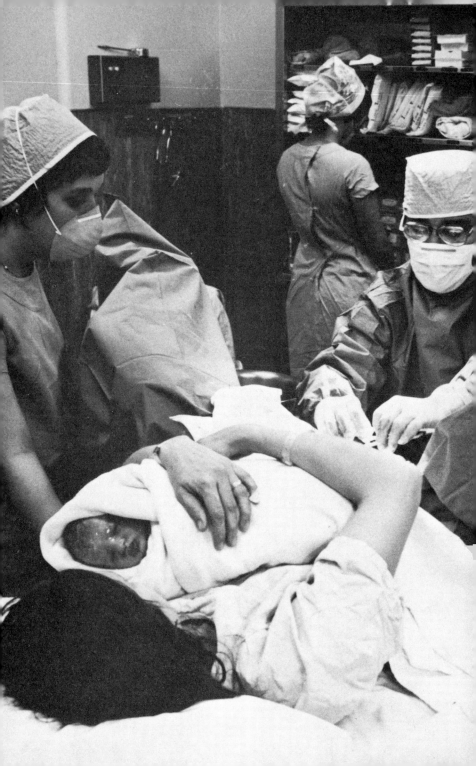

3 / The Delivery: When and Where

Two of the more contentious issues in modern obstetric practice are, first, the question of induction of labor: is it really necessary and, if so, when should it be done? Second, is a hospital the best place to have a baby or can some deliveries take place at home? The issues are difficult because they involve the questions of the role of the doctor in our society, the value attributed to scientific findings, and the way these findings are used.

Some of the problems arise from the fact that, thanks to contraception and abortion, we have a markedly decreasing birthrate and, thanks to better social conditions and better obstetrics, a decreasing deathrate for mothers and babies at the time of birth. A hundred years ago parents accepted the fact that many of their children would die at an early age. But now, along with considerable pressure for the number of offspring per family to be limited to two, there is widespread expectation that these children should live and be normal and healthy. It is only the present low deathrate at birth that allows us even to begin to consider the emotional quality of the experience and the long-term psychological consequences.

The new focus on these matters has resulted in an increasingly idealized insistence that pregnancy and delivery should not only be perfect as far as the physical health of mother and baby are concerned, but also that the experience should be perfect emotionally. Unfortunately these two attainments, given the current state of medicine, may not always be compatible. This does not mean that the ideal should not be sought, but the effort has to be tempered with the realization that perfection may not be possible.

It then comes to a question of values. Do we think that physiological perfection should be bought at the expense of possible psychological disadvantage, or are parents willing to take certain risks of physical damage in exchange for better emotional results? The situation is made all the more complicated by the fact that these decisions are made on behalf of the child as well, which puts vast responsibility on those concerned. We have to take into account what statistics are available. For instance, in medical research, relationships are often shown to exist between two factors. If a baby is in the uterus for more than forty-two weeks, there is an increased incidence of injury to him. This association may be definite but low: say five out of a hundred babies who prolong their stay in the uterus until forty-three weeks may suffer some kind of trouble. It may be impossible to determine which five babies out of the hundred will be the ones who suffer and which ninety-five will not. It is here that a value judgment is made. Do we induce a hundred babies to make sure that five will not suffer physical damage? And knowing that ninety-five babies will be induced without their needing it, are we exposing them in turn to the small risk of side-effects from the procedure?

In most cases the doctor is in the best position to know what the risks are, but it is also here that his role may be called into question. He can try and explain to the parents what the risks are, so that they can be involved in making an informed decision. Or he can act as an authority who thinks that he understands all the processes at work and is therefore justified in telling the parents what is going to happen and allowing them little role in the decision. In England the freedom of choice is slightly greater than in the United States. In many states in America, women are already bound by law to have their children in a hospital, attended by a doctor. In England, they still have the choice of home delivery, with a midwife, though in many areas this choice has become more theoretical than practical because domicilary services are being phased out.

INDUCTION

The mechanism by which labor gets underway is still a mystery, though this is not from lack of investigation but from the

complexity of the processes involved. Normally at forty weeks after conception, give or take two weeks, uterine contractions will begin spontaneously. It is now thought that when the brain of the baby reaches a certain state of maturity, it releases a substance that begins a chain of reactions finally leading to delivery. It is obvious though, that a number of other factors are also involved.

It is possible to change this biological clock by medical induction. The methods commonly used are: first, artificially rupturing the membranous sac containing baby and amniotic fluid. This is done with surgical instruments, through the vagina and cervix, and sometimes also involves stripping the membranes away from the walls of the uterus. Second, administering a variety of drugs, either by mouth, by injection, or by intravenous drip. This last method is most popular because uterine contractions can be controlled by the rate at which the drug is administered into the vein. Third, introducing a drug directly into the uterus with a catheter. The drugs normally used are oxytocin, which has been available for a number of years and acts mainly by causing contractions, and the prostaglandins, which are becoming increasingly popular and act by causing both uterine contractions and cervical dilation. It is thought that none of these methods of induction bears much relationship to the mechanisms by which labor begins spontaneously.

Another relevant factor concerning induction is the state of the cervix. Before being delivered the baby obviously has to pass through the cervix, and it is now usual when induction is performed to assess the cervical condition by manual examination through the vagina. The cervix may be "ripe," when it is soft enough to allow easy passage of the baby, or it may still be hard and offer considerable resistance. Softening of the cervix normally occurs when the baby is near its full term in the uterus, as the result of hormones produced in the body. Although drugs may also affect softening, inductions done when the cervix is hard tend to be more painful and hazardous.

There are medical indications for inducing labor which are undoubtedly life-saving, and in these cases it is obvious that any detrimental emotional or behavioral effects will be of secondary importance. There is no question, when in certain cases induction is an absolute necessity, that this judgment rests largely with

the doctor, who then has the responsibility of explaining the reasons to the parents. But the amount of disagreement that exists over such indications can be seen by looking at the rates at which women are induced in different obstetrical units. In some hospitals six to seven women out of every ten are induced, and there are obstetricians who advise all women to be induced; on the other hand, some units have induction rates of one or two out of ten. So there is a rate variation of at least between 10 percent and 70 percent in units dealing with similar mothers.

What are the advantages and disadvantages of induction? The absolute advantage is that in some cases it saves the mother or the child from death or damage. Some of the other more arguable advantages are that the mother is well rested; her stomach is empty because food can be restricted, which decreases danger if a general anesthetic has to be given; last-minute transport problems to a hospital are avoided; the mother is able to organize her life more efficiently if she knows when the delivery is going to occur.

There are philosophical as well as medical arguments against induction. The processes involved in birth have developed over millions of years; they are extremely complicated and our state of knowledge about them is still rudimentary. If one is going to interfere with such processes, one must not only be aware of the benefits but also continually investigate the side-effects, knowing that these may appear much later. Second, childbirth is an important emotional event in many people's lives (in Britain about 80 percent of the population become parents); if birth is to be controlled by specialists, using mechanical means, in large institutions, then it may sometimes adversely affect the development of confidence and the emotional development of the parents in their relationship with their child. No good long-term studies to judge these effects have been completed, though some are underway.

Of other possible disadvantages, several studies have shown that babies born to mothers who have been induced with oxytocin run a slightly higher risk of becoming jaundiced than babies born spontaneously. Heinz Prechtl, working in Holland, has shown that jaundice alters the behavior of the baby; while it lasts the baby tends to sleep more and to spend less time alert.[1]

Other studies have clearly indicated that mothers who have been induced need to have more pain-killing drugs than those who have not been. The effects of some of these drugs on the behavior of the baby are discussed later, but suffice it to say here that they do in some cases significantly alter the baby's behavior after birth.

There is also the question of separation of mother and baby immediately after birth. Studies indicate that the incidence of babies admitted to special-care units, away from their mothers, is considerably higher when birth is induced. Of course, these babies may have to go into special care not because of the induction but because of a reason that led to the induction in the first place. But a study done at Cambridge University, of a relatively small number of women and their babies, found little relation between medical or social reasons for induction and the rate at which the babies were admitted to special care.[2] The rate of admission of induced babies of both sorts was 34.4 percent, whereas the admission rate for noninduced babies was 17.4. In another study done in England, Sheila Kitzinger examined the reports sent in by mothers who attended the National Childbirth Trust classes.[3] Her results cannot be applied generally since this group of women might have been especially motivated toward natural childbirth, but she found that 24 percent of the induced babies had gone into special care as opposed to only 7 percent of the noninduced babies. There is no way of telling whether these admissions were related to the induction itself or to the reasons behind the inductions.

What about the subjective experiences of mothers? Not unexpectedly, the results are conflicting. In one study carried out by M. Ounstead, four groups of mothers were included: a group induced by intravenous oxytocin, a group induced by intravenous prostaglandins, a group induced by putting prostaglandins directly into the uterus, and a control group that was not induced. In all there were 235 mothers having first babies (and here again more babies from the induced group went to the special-care unit). On the day after delivery the women were asked whether labor and delivery were better, worse, or the same as anticipated. Of those giving a definite "better" or "worse" answer 78 percent of the induced group said the labor

was better than expected, compared with 59 percent of the non-induced group. The answers about delivery revealed no difference between the groups. Followed up after four months, 76 of the original induced mothers were asked whether they would like to have an induction again: 24 percent said yes, 25 percent said they would not mind, and 51 percent said they did not want one again. These results have to be viewed against the fact that these mothers had no previous experience of childbirth as a basis for comparison.

In contrast to this, Kitzinger looked at the reports of 53 mothers who were induced and had delivered previous babies.[4] Of these, 30 percent said the induced labor was better than the previous labor; 64 percent thought it worse. The remaining 6 percent found it about the same. In a control group of noninduced mothers with previous babies, 96 percent said their labor was better than the previous labor. Now, as I have pointed out, the trouble with this study is that the women already had a moderately strong desire for natural delivery, and therefore it could be argued that their reports of their labors as worse than their previous ones should be taken not so much as a condemnation of induction itself as an expression of their failure to fulfill a desire for spontaneous delivery.

In the Cambridge study already mentioned, induced women having their first babies were asked about inductions before and after they delivered. The percentage who disliked induction increased from 45 before delivery to 74 after. For those who had delivered previous babies, the figures were 64.5 percent before and 69 percent after. There were several reasons given for not wanting inductions: the speed of labor prevents the body from acclimatizing itself, so that contractions are more painful; induction detracts from the birth experience because the speed makes the reality of the birth hard to accept; the quick succession of pains lead to panic, so that breathing control is lost; induction detracts from the excitement of labor; it leaves a feeling of having been somehow cheated.

In most of these studies, no attempt was made to differentiate between induction and speeded deliveries. Induction is, technically, simply the starting of labor; in speeded deliveries the drugs used to start labor are continued to keep the uterine contractions going.

HOME VERSUS HOSPITAL

In all discussions of home versus hospital delivery, the child-birth practices in the Netherlands inevitably come up. Holland has a lower deathrate among babies than either the United States or England, and yet a very substantial number of the deliveries are carried out at home.

G. J. Kloosterman, Professor of Obstetrics at the University of Amsterdam, has summarized the philosophy on which the organization of obstetrics in the Netherlands has been based since the beginning of this century.[5] "Childbirth in itself is a natural phenomenon and in the large majority of cases needs no interference whatsoever—only close observation, moral support, and protection against human meddling." A healthy woman who delivers spontaneously performs a job that cannot be improved upon. This job can be done in the best way if the woman is self-confident and stays in surroundings where she is the real center (as in her own home) It is possible during pregnancy, by thorough prenatal care, to divide expectant mothers into two groups: a large one that shows no recognizable symptoms of pathology (the so-called low-risk group) and a much smaller one in which there are signs of slight or even gross abnormalities. Only the high-risk group belongs in a good hospital under the care of specialists; the other is better off under the care of specialists in the physiology of childbirth, the midwife, or a general practitioner with special training in obstetrics.

In 1973, 196,974 babies were born in Holland, and of these approximately 99,000 were born at home. Great emphasis is put on the benefits of an organization called Maternity Home Help, whose purposes are to provide assistance during the delivery; to provide care for mother and child for eight to ten days after confinement; and to train home helpers to take the mother's place in the family during the lying-in period. In 1973, of the 99,000 home deliveries, 83,088 were attended by a home helper, midwives, or doctors with the cooperation of home helpers. The deathrate of the babies delivered at home was less than one third of the overall rate for the whole of the Netherlands, 4.5 per 1000 as against 16.3 per 1000 births.

The philosophy in Great Britain and the United States is quite different. It operates on the basis that it is impossible to predict

which women will be "at risk," so that all women having babies must be treated as if they were high risks and hospitals are the places to deal with them. Therefore, if a mother has her baby at home, she is increasing the risks not only to her own health but to that of the baby. Again a question of values is involved. Each time a pregnant woman crosses a street she is increasing the risk of death for herself and her unborn baby, but no one would question her right to cross the street.

Is there any evidence that it makes a long-term difference if a baby is delivered at home or in the hospital? Hard scientific evidence is difficult to come by, and there probably never will be any definitive studies done because the associated issues are so many and so complex. There is some evidence that the incidence of depression after birth is increased in hospital deliveries. In one study the figures were that some depression occurred in 60 percent of hospital deliveries and in only 16 percent of home deliveries. It is also interesting to note that in a study of 601,222 spontaneous deliveries, there was a peak of births at 3:00 to 4:00 A.M., a time when the woman is likely to be in a quiet sheltered environment and in a sleepily peaceful emotional state; interestingly enough, the onset of labor also showed a peak at night.

With the reminder that one should always be very cautious about applying findings from studies of animals to human behavior, I want to review some of the evidence that environment affects labor in animals. Observation of animals in their natural habitat shows that many species seek out quiet and familiar surroundings in which to have their babies.[6] In one experiment, systematic work with artificial situations have been carried out with mice. Toward the end of pregnancy they were moved every half hour between a familiar nesting box and a glass bowl with rock bedding. Significantly more first births took place in the nesting box and, in general, significantly more pups were born in the familiar environment than in the glass bowl. In a further study, after the birth of their second pup in a litter, the mice were gently disturbed by a complete change of the smell and touch sensations of the environment. After this, the average labor time before the birth of the next pup in the litter was more than twenty minutes. In a similar but undisturbed group of mice used for comparison, it was only twelve or thirteen minutes. A third study involved three experimental groups of mice: toward the

end of pregnancy, one group was given continuous disturbance, one periodic disturbance, and the third minimal disturbance. These environmental differences all influenced the time of arrival of the first pup, the timing of births in the later part of labor, and the number of pups who died in each group. Although comparable experiments with human beings have not been undertaken, for the obvious reasons, clinical observations of women during labor seem to indicate that environmental disturbances may affect the timing, strength, and efficiency of contractions.

Finally I would like to quote from a talk given by a pediatrician, John Davies, to a National Childbirth Trust seminar on home deliveries. He pointed out that there were positive and negative sides to every human activity: "Nobody goes to sea only to sick . . . I feel very strongly myself that there is no point in a child being conceived, born and reared, unless birth has that positive side to it by which it is recognized as something adult human beings need and want to do in order to 'be themselves.' " There is no way to prove by statistics that a baby born at home is any better off than one born in hospital but:

> I do not think that the collection of figures to support a case is science. We are not dealing with matters that are susceptible to statistical analysis. I saw some of my children born at home and some born in excellent hospitals, and my personal experience squares with that of many women, that where you compare one experience that has gone well with another that has gone as well as it can, the quality of the experience at home is superior to that of the other. I cannot speak for the quality of the experience for the baby. Of course babies do not have memories that make them able to describe what was going on in the labour ward when they first opened their eyes. But there may be another, less systematized, kind of memory and it does not mean that the experience has been lost, or is not having an influence. Being received into a normal home where the mother is in command and at ease, and where the other children not only know but feel that the baby is a real addition to their family (and not brought back from Harrods, or whatever fantasy they may construct of the event), is likely to be the best way to enter life.

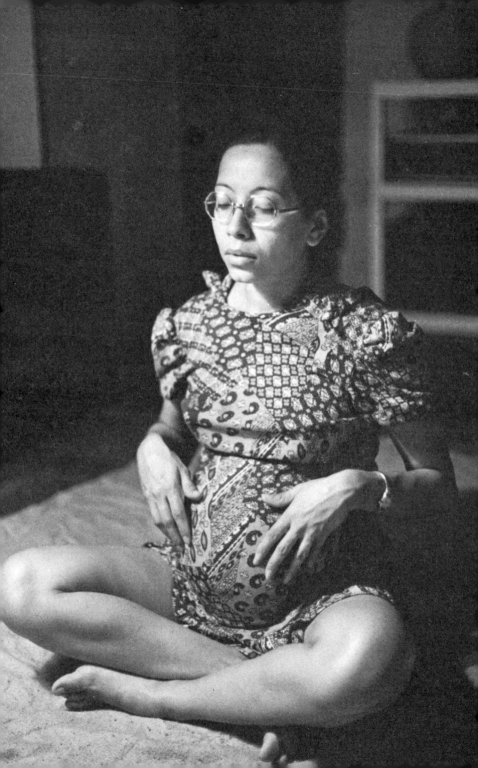

4 / Pain and Relief

Pain is a sensation that normally serves us well. If we get a splinter, pain encourages us to remove it before any damage occurs. In this context pain obviously has a survival value. But what about the pain of childbirth? Reproduction is vital to the survival of any species and it seems strange that, in humans and higher animals, birth is so often associated with extreme pain, for this might be thought to have a discouraging effect. That it doesn't may be a tribute to the pleasures of sex or the shortness of people's memory about pain in childbirth. But why, considering the usual course of natural selection, should birth be associated with pain? Why is it there? And does it perform any function?

It was a popular theory thirty years ago that the pains of childbirth were a feature of modern society and that women in primitive cultures did not feel them. The idea gained ground that, if we could become "natural" again, our society too could return to a state where childbirth was pain-free. But observation of people still living in primitive societies around the world appears to show that there is no culture in which childbirth is painless, and in many cultures women have a much worse time than in our own. As Margaret Mead puts it, "Childbirth may be experienced according to the phrasing given it by the culture, as an experience that is dangerous and painful, interesting and engrossing, matter of fact and mildly hazardous, or accompanied by enormous supernatural hazards."[1]

Anatomically it should have been possible for us to develop as a species without nerves that send pain sensations from the uterus, vagina, or perineum. The last two are exquisitely sensi-

tive to pleasure sensations, and it may be that pain fibers (which are separate from nerves carrying pleasure sensations) are necessary in these areas in order to protect them from damage. If this is so, then they are going to be hugely stimulated by the infant's head passing through what is normally a relatively narrow canal.

What of animals? Do they suffer during childbirth and, if so, what effect does it have? Eugene Marais, in *The Soul of the Ape*,[2] makes a point that has also been noted by others: in lower animals the process of reproduction is as simple as it is painless; it is only in higher animals, with their greatly reduced birthrates, that we meet the first indications of birth pain; and as a sure and proportionate accompaniment, we find a need for maternal care of the immature young. Experiments with animals that do experience pain in childbirth show that in certain species, drugs given to remove pain alter behavior toward the young after birth. Marais observed a herd of buck in which, for fifteen years, there had been no case of a mother's refusing to look after her young under normal conditions. He took ten of the animals and made them either totally or partially unconscious with drugs during delivery, allowing them to recover shortly afterwards. In all cases these animals rejected their newborns and refused to mother them. He took another group of animals and made them unconscious just after birth for about thirty minutes; these animals did not reject their newborns. It would be very dangerous to draw any definite conclusions from these findings about how humans behave or, for that matter, how other animals behave. For instance, a goat made unconscious just after delivery and then given its newborn would undoubtedly reject it; in this species the period just after birth is vital for the development of nurturing. It is possible, however, to put forward the theory that pain, along with many other processes, does play some part in the development of a mother's feelings for her baby.

Another theory of the use of pain is that it may serve in some way to help keep mothers alert during labor and in the period immediately after delivery. Many mothers and babies who have gone through a normal labor and delivery without drugs also experience an hour or two of extreme alertness following delivery. In terms of muscle usage labor is fantastically exhausting, and it may be that pain counteracts the sensations of fatigue.

This could be mediated by hormones, for Russian researchers have found that the secretion of adrenaline appears to be related to feelings of pain.

In humans, there are at least two contributing factors to the sensation of pain. First there is the nerve message to the brain following stimulation or damage to some area of the body. Second there is the state of the brain when it receives the message, and this is affected by cultural expectations about pain, previous experience of it, anxiety, fear, fatigue, and expectations about the outcome of the pain. If you hit your finger with a hammer, pain predicts a bruised finger. In labor, pain predicts the birth of a baby.

People differ greatly in their anatomy and physiology, so there are individual differences in the number of pain messages reaching the brain. Thus some women have totally painless births, no matter what conditions prevail. These are commonly said to total between 7 and 14 percent of all women, though I personally find that figure very high and suspect that 3 or 4 percent would be more accurate. But there is still a great deal of debate about how, when pain messages reach the brain, they are altered by psychological factors. It is hard to measure pain in an objective way. Researchers have attempted to measure pain by looking at associated changes in body functions, such as dilation of the pupil, speed up of the pulse, changes in blood flow through the skin, and changes in blood pressure. These have proved unreliable. In any case, objective measurement may not be very helpful if what matters is how pain is perceived.

Some people have tried to use certain kinds of behavior, such as grimacing, grinding the teeth, frequent crying out, or tears, as indicators of the severity of pain; but behavior is almost totally dependent on cultural expectations about what people do in pain. It is, after all, fairly frequent in our society that an obstetrician delivers a woman in what he thinks is an ideal, uncomplicated, and straightforward way, only to learn that she has found the whole thing utterly harrowing. The reverse is also true. (Unfortunately this sometimes leads a doctor to disbelieve a mother, or at least to feel she is exaggerating, on the grounds that her observations do not coincide with his own. But there is no reason why they should, for the birth is being seen from two very different vantages, and expectations of acceptable behavior

need in no way coincide.) Recently researchers in Wales did an experiment where women in labor were asked to squeeze an object during each contraction according to how much pain they were having. The object they squeezed was attached to a recording machine that measured how much pressure the woman was exerting. What they discovered was that, very early on in labor, the women were already squeezing as hard as they possibly could and therefore were unable to squeeze any harder later, even if the pain grew worse.

The psychological aspects of pain have been demonstrated in various other ways. For instance, if people being tested for the maximum level of pain they can stand are given an injection of sterile water which they are told is a pain killer, they will in many cases report an increased tolerance to pain even though the water itself could not have helped.[3] This is the so-called placebo effect.

For the last twenty years researchers in the Soviet Union have been studying the effects of psychoprophylaxis (psychological and physical preparation by instruction and practice) and hypnosis on the pain of childbirth. These methods induce relaxation during birth in order to prevent the muscles of the pelvis from tensing up and thus making the uterine contractions less effective and the pressure against the pelvic tissues greater. The methods thus decrease the amount of pain messages going to the brain, and they might also alter the woman's perceptions or her ability to control such messages when they did get to the brain. The overall finding from the Soviet research, which has been based on observations of many thousands of mothers during delivery, is that psychoprophylaxis and hypnosis both decrease not only the pain of childbirth but also the incidence of birth complications. In many of their studies the Russians have used a five-point scale to judge the amount of pain: (5) maximum success, no pain, the mother conscious and active throughout the labor, (4) complaints of short duration with endurable pain, (3) failure in spite of some temporary pain relief, (2) and (1) complete failure. In one study of five hundred women, comparing psychoprophylaxis with drugs, the failure rate (that is, women in groups 3, 2, and 1) was 47 percent with drugs—this was before the days of epidural anesthesia—and 33 percent with psychoprophylaxis.[4]

Another recent and unpublished study done by C. Fisher in England examines pain-killing drugs given during labor when antenatal care, delivery, and early mother-child care after delivery were all handled by a single person—a midwife—with deliveries either done at home or in the general-practitioner unit attached to the local maternity hospital. One hundred consecutive births were analyzed: of the 55 women having their first baby 21 (38 percent) needed no drugs, and of the 45 having their second, third, or fourth babies, 38 (84 percent) needed no drugs. The comparable figures for the maternity unit of the same hospital show a very much higher usage of pain-killing drugs.

METHODS OF RELIEF

Be they chemical, psychological, or magical, attempts to relieve the pain of childbirth are probably as old as humanity. In our own culture, the methods used include drugs, psychoprophylaxis, hypnosis, and acupuncture.

Drugs. Drugs to help with birth pain were first used in England in 1847 by James Young Simpson, who used ether. Six years later Queen Victoria gave birth to Prince Leopold under chloroform administered by John Snow, and she was said to show approval. Since then a huge variety of chemical substances have been inhaled, swallowed, and injected into various parts of the body in an effort to deal effectively with pain in labor and delivery.

The method now employed with most frequent success in both England and the United States is epidural anesthesia. A local anesthetic is introduced into the space around the spinal cord with a needle or tube; the drug blocks the transmission of messages along the nerves carrying sensation from the legs and abdomen. This anesthetic does not appear to interfere with uterine contractions, though the mechanisms by which the baby is actually delivered may not be as efficient (several studies of epidural deliveries indicate an increased need for the use of forceps). Its other advantage is that it has little effect on the level of consciousness of the mother; she can be aware of the course of delivery even if, because of the loss of sensation, less able to participate actively. The method is in most cases both effective and

safe. The drugs, however, do enter the mother's bloodstream and via the placenta enter the baby's blood too; one recent study indicates that for a period after birth some of these babies may have decreased muscle strength and tone.[5]

Pethidine (meperidine, demerol) has for the last ten years, before the advent of epidurals, held prime place among drugs. It is frequently used in combination with another drug, levallorphan, which counteracts the effects that pethidine has on breathing. How exactly pethidine works is difficult to assess, for it is a morphia derivative and causes very definite changes in consciousness and in the way the outside world is perceived. Many mothers describe the sensation as "feeling drunk," "being out of control," "feeling very drowsy and distant." Whether it acts by altering the perception of pain once the messages have reached the brain, or whether it actually decreases the messages reaching the brain, is difficult to tell. A study done at one London hospital attempted to assess how good a pain killer pethidine was.[6] Three groups of pregnant women were given a test to see what their pain threshold was. Pressure was applied to the skin covering the bone in the front of the lower leg. The groups were then either given an injection of sterile water, pethidine alone, or pethidine and levallorphan, and then tested again at varying intervals to see if their pain threshold had changed. In all three groups the threshold remained virtually the same, with only minor variations, and the peculiar conclusion of the study was that pressure on the lower leg was not a suitable way of judging the effects of drugs on labor pains. But other studies have indicated that pethidine does have a pain-killing effect, and this surely must be so or its use would have never continued at the rate it has.

The effects of drugs on both mother and baby have always been extremely carefully monitored by the medical profession and others, and the importance of this was emphasized in the 1960s when it was discovered that barbiturates given to mothers during labor tended to depress respiration in babies. They were abandoned, but previously, while they were still in use, the pediatrician Berry Brazelton found that babies born to mothers who had had barbiturates were reported to be poor at sucking and difficult to feed.[7] He also discovered that they were slower in gaining weight than babies born to mothers without drugs.

Other work has shown that babies born under barbiturates sucked slower, with less pressure, and took less at each feeding. At about the same time, Gerald Stechler was doing some research on perception that involved finding out what babies aged two to four days liked to look at.[8] He presented them with three cards; on one was printed the outline of a face, on the second three dots, and on the third nothing. They looked most at the one with the face, less at the three dots, and least at the blank card. Although this is interesting in itself, what is significant here is that babies born to mothers under barbiturates (and also under pethidine) looked at the cards less than those babies born to mothers without drugs. This is perhaps not very surprising since the drugs alter one's state of consciousness, and when they are injected they rapidly cross over the placenta to the baby. Drugs do stay in babies longer than in adults because babies are less equipped to get rid of them in the usual way, by breaking them down into other substances and then peeing them out. But why effects should last for several days and even longer is still the subject of much speculation.

These findings greatly intrigued psychologists, who followed them up with their own observations of babies. Yvonne Brackbill specifically looked at the effect of pethidine on babies.[9] She had examined, first, its effect on what some people regard as the most primitive form of learning in babies: habituation, by which a baby (or anyone else) comes to take no notice of some stimulation he initially found disturbing. Brackbill played a relatively loud sound to babies in short bursts over and over again, to see how long they would take to stop reacting to it. Babies born to the pethidine mothers took over twice as long to stop reacting to the noise as those babies born to non-pethidine mothers. In another study they tended to be less responsive in turning toward the sound of a voice, were less cuddly, and less consolable when they cried. Martin Richards and Judy Dunn found that babies born under the pethidine and levallorphan mixture showed altered sucking behavior.[10] If a baby showed differences in behavior, they thought, this might affect his mother's way of responding to him. They observed the mothers feeding their babies and found that indeed the pethidine mothers had to stimulate their babies more during each feeding and that the feedings were shorter and more often interrupted. It is not yet clear what

the longer-term significance of this might be. I have myself over the last few years made a large number of observations on babies to see how much they can see, hear, and smell, and what kinds of things they like to see, hear, and smell. In every case I have looked to see whether the drug used during delivery had an effect, and in only one so far have I found this to be so: in my study of whether babies can tell where a voice is coming from, babies of pethidine mothers generally performed less well.[11]

To turn quickly to other well-known methods of relief: Inhalants, such as nitrous oxide, which have now been used for some time, seem to alter the consciousness of the mother for a short period and so far have not been shown to have a significant effect on the behavior of the baby. With general anesthesia, when the mother is made completely unconscious, the drugs do cross the placenta and will affect some of the baby's functions, but little research has been done on this so far. What has been done indicates that the babies are affected by the anesthetic agents for a period of time after birth.

With the knowledge now available, new drugs are going through much more exhaustive testing, but it is of course only too likely that chemical substances introduced into the body will have effects other than the desired one. In light of our assessment of the need for drugs in childbirth, it is extremely interesting to compare the rate of use in different countries. According to recent surveys, drugs are given for pain in only 5 percent of deliveries in Holland and in 12 percent of deliveries in Sweden. Equivalent drugs are given in more than 80 percent of deliveries in England. English women are not particularly noted to be any less stoical than their European counterparts—but why is there this huge difference? Is it because English doctors and midwives feel that drugs should be given routinely? Or could it be that Dutch and Swedish women know childbirth is going to be painful but accept pain as part of the whole process, whereas English women have been conditioned to believe that pain must be relieved?

Psychoprophylaxis. We have already met this method in the context of Soviet research. Its aim is to teach women the processes, both physical and mental, that occur during pregnancy, labor, delivery, and the early moments of the baby's life, so that

they will feel able to control and help their own bodies' actions. It is an essentially active venture: the mother controls the labor and delivers her child, with others there to assist when asked.

Quite independently of the work in the USSR, in 1933 Grantly Dick-Read published *Childbirth Without Fear* to show how women could aid childbirth by learning how to relax.[12] Fear and anxiety, he proposed, cause tension, and tension causes pain. In the 1940s Fernand Lamaze, a French obstetrician working in a Communist trade-union clinic in Paris, traveled to Russia and brought back the idea that women who had been properly instructed in pregnancy could actively control their labor delivery. His assumption was that childbirth is an essentially psychosomatic process and that both psychological and physical preparation are essential. Since then, within the "natural childbirth" movement, the emphasis put on the mind or on the body has varied, from country to country and from one time to another.

In the simplest of terms, current methods used to teach natural childbirth endeavor to instill confidence in the mother by instructing her, and generally her husband too, in the actual physiological processes of pregnancy and birth. A series of classes are taught to give her an understanding and control of the changes occurring in her body. The groups are usually headed by a trained instructor, and an important part of the instruction is hearing the experience of others. The methods include practice of special breathing exercises, which are keyed to the uterine contractions typical of the different stages of labor.

The pain-reducing procedures generally taught throughout the world are techniques that aid the mother in maintaining control; and techniques that can be practiced during confinement to relax the muscles and collaborate actively with the expulsive efforts. The studies made in the USSR strongly support the idea that such preparation both reduces pain and improves obstetrics. In Great Britain and the United States, however, it has been found that such studies are very difficult to assess. The main argument against their reliability is that a certain kind of woman (usually middle-class in our culture) is disposed toward psychoprophylaxis, perhaps because of education, greater leisure, and so on, and that any differences found between those using this method for dealing with pain and those using other methods may be due to the personalities of the women rather than to the

method itself. Ideally, to get around this, a study would have to be arranged in which mothers were randomly assigned to have psychoprophylaxis or some other method of pain killing, but quite rightly that would be unacceptable on ethical grounds. However, studies done in many Western countries indicate that women who have had psychoprophylactic training do in fact get fewer drugs. I use the word "get" deliberately because, for them, getting fewer drugs is probably dependent on several factors. For instance, they may actually feel less pain, or they may feel that it would be a waste of their training if they allowed themselves to be given drugs, or it may just be that they are better able to refuse drugs in cases where they are routinely administered. Since the husband is included in the instruction, he can support his wife in all these matters.

At present the main development in psychoprophylaxis is toward better emotional and psychological preparation. For example, Sheila Kitzinger's book *The Experience of Childbirth* integrates birth into the whole course of a woman's sexual development. Her method might therefore be called "psychosexual."[13]

Hypnosis and acupuncture. Hypnosis is a reversible mental state, produced in one person by another, that involves an increased susceptibility to suggestion which can lead to sensory and physical changes. Methods of using hypnosis in childbirth vary: some use posthypnotic suggestion, others have delivered the child while the mother is actually hypnotized. Many argue about whether the pain of childbirth is actually reduced by this method or whether it simply produces a memory block against recalling the pain; but hypnosis does not in fact automatically block the memory of events, so there may be a real reduction. Again, Russian researchers have claimed that the method is effective, although a recent study of a very large number of consecutive deliveries in women who had been given hypnotic conditioning found that only 7 percent of them had painless births— a figure, you will remember, comparable to that claimed for unprepared women. Leon Chertok, in his book on psychosomatic methods, thinks that hypnosis, suggestion, and psychoprophylaxis operate by similar means in affecting the experience of pain in labor.[14] He regards "suggestion" as the common factor in all these techniques, though feels that other effects may also be involved.

Recently there has been a resurgence of interest in acupuncture as a means of relieving birth pain, but it has been noted that, although Chinese textbooks on the subject indicate that acupuncture can be used for the treatment of such obstetric complications as a prolonged second stage of labor, there is relatively little written about relieving pain. One reason for this might be that, although acupuncture has been used in China for a thousand years therapeutically, its use for operative pain killing is fairly recent.

Moxacombustion, the burning of some kind of moxa (usually *Artemesia vulgaris*) at an acupuncture site, is the discipline's recommended method for the relief of childbirth pain. Though few deliveries are now being done in the West using these methods, they are becoming more popular. One report on fifteen cases claimed complete success in six cases and six complete failures; but these last women, it was thought, were either too fat or too frightened. Nonetheless, there are some who are confident that acupuncture will play an important role in pain relief during childbirth.

TRANSCRIPT: MRS. A, AGED 25, FIRST BABY (A GIRL)

Father	Mother	Midwife
		Oops, oops. Show her. It's a little girl—welcome darling.
Wow, there she is! Didn't take very long to come out, did you?	Oh lovely, oh lovely. Oh, a cough.	
	Oh, that was nice.	Very nice.
	Oh, that was very nice. A hiccough. That was the sherry last night.	There, look.
Ah, oh, was it?	Hello.	
(laughs)	Oh dear, what a lot of noise.	Well, if that was the sherry, you must have had a lot of sherry last night.
Yes.	Oh.	Two little bits under the arms there.

No vernix.

Oh, how nice.

What a funny-coloured beast.

It's not a funny colour. It's very nice.

What a big one, isn't it?

I'm very satisfied.

(laughs) Are you satisfied?

Oh dear—just floods all over the place. Just try to keep out of it for a moment.

Oh well, that's a nice normal beast, isn't it. Hello.

(baby given to mother)

Oh, hello. Hello. Oh, you're nice. That's a lot of noise for a little girl. That's right—you've opened your eyes. That's lovely.

Oh, that's good, that's very good. That's a very good and nice noise.

Miaow.

No, not miaow, that's the other sort.

That's nice.

Father	*Mother*	*Midwife*
	Oh you're nice. What a nice beast. Oh, a hiccough. Oh, a hiccough.	
Aah! Well done—it was clever of you. It only took six hours and ten minutes. That's very clever.		
	Oh.	Has she got a name, actually?
Christina Margaret.		
	To be known as Kirsty, we hope.	How nice.
	Hello. Do you like it? Well, don't squeeze your face up like that. What a silly thing to do. We'll call you Albert if you're not careful.	
Aah, miaow.		
	Ow!	
She's got nice skin.		
	Very nice skin—pretty colour too.	
Mmm—virginal white.		
	Oh.	

Oh, not very nice though, is it?

Not yet. Yes, you have lovely lungs.

Mmm. Hasn't opened its eyes. What colour are its eyes?

I don't know what colour.

Got the shakes?

I had the shakes all the time since last night.

Oh, you are a beautiful baby.

Absolutely babylike too. Born to all these strange-shaped heads and things. You are perfectly normal.

Oh, oh. You're not a Cameron at all.

There's not another one inside, is there?

There isn't, no. A hiccough.

Do you want me to go and make the phone call?

Yes. Sorry—that was the noise I was making because I was being sick.

Father	Mother	Midwife
She's a very good-looking child. What colour are your eyes? Blue, she says. Aah, waah (*imitates baby crying*).		
	We were determined. We had avocado pear with rather nice mustardy sauce, and the wienerschnitzel and broccoli and sauté potatoes, followed by chocolate charlotte.	That will teach you. Serve you right when you are beginning to go into labour.
	I didn't really think. I thought I was due Wednesday so I noshed up whilst I could.	Yes!
	I'm sorry I'm shaking, little beasty.	
	You're a big beasty, mind you. Oh (*imitates baby*). Oh (*imitates baby*). What a shame, what a shame.	Fancy calling your daughter a little beasty!

That was water and an unusual amount of it.

She looks like her grandmother.

It's rather a mess, isn't it. She's got fabulous eyelashes.

See how her colour is changing.

It's nice—got my nose and my ears. Not at all yours.

Rubbish. Oh!

Well, I think we'll have to tell Charity you've had a girl.

Do you fancy a green apple? I brought you one 'cause you said you wanted one.

I'm sorry, I can't pull it out because I shall cause a tidal wave (*to baby*). Oh, that's a nice tongue.

Oh, I probably shan't.

Bend your legs up, love.

I'm sorry about my legs shaking.

That's all right—you can't help it.

It's a bit hard with the sheet there.

OK.

Push. Come on, bit harder.

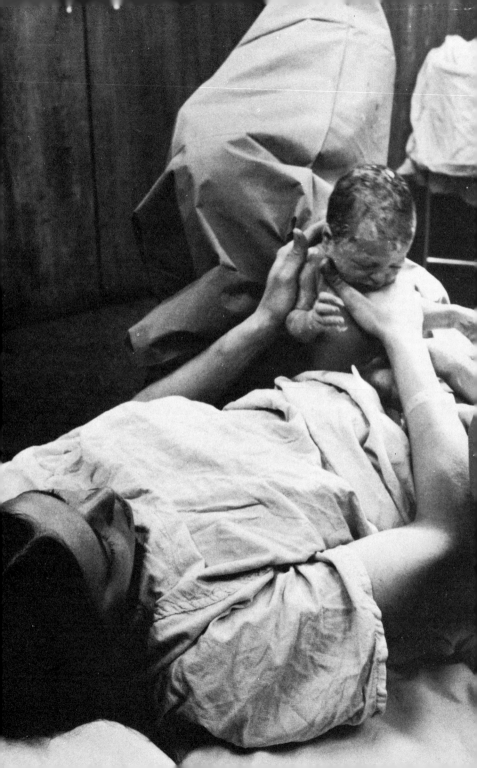

5 / The First Minutes

After the long months of watching and feeling an abdomen slowly enlarging, of being aware of the changing movements of the fetus, of experiencing labor and delivery—which has been likened to climbing to the top of a very high mountain—what then of that first moment after birth when parents and baby meet one another face to face? What are the mother's feelings when she first actually sees the child of her own flesh and blood, the child she already knows so intimately and for whom she will be responsible for at least the next fifteeen years?

The normal routine in hospitals after the baby is born varies considerably, but in general the cord is cut and tied, the baby's mouth and throat are cleared of any fluid, and the baby is wrapped up and observed for a short period to ensure that regular breathing has been established and that he is a good color. Upon birth, it is common for whoever is handling the baby to record his heartrate, muscle tone, and breathing and color. This "Apgar score" serves as a permanent record of the baby's condition and can be used for reference later if necessary. Then, still well wrapped up (heat loss from the skin of the baby is so rapid that his temperature can drop very fast), the baby is handed to the mother.

In this book I have included transcripts of a series of deliveries recorded on videotape as part of a research project I was doing to find out how mothers and babies got to know one another's needs over the first few months after birth. I talked to the mothers when they were about thirty-six weeks' pregnant with their first baby. At that time I asked them what they expected labor and delivery to be like, as well as how they thought they would

51

care for the baby later: I was interested to see how actually having a baby would change these ideas. All the mothers had uncomplicated pregnancies and volunteered to take part.

In looking at the mother's and baby's behavior in the delivery room, I was following up some marvelous work done in the United States by pediatricians Marshall Klaus and John Kennell.[1] They had filmed twelve mothers with their full-term infants some time between thirty minutes and thirteen hours after birth. In order to allow the mother maximum freedom in handling her baby, both mother and baby were put under a radiant heater so that the baby could be naked with no fear of his getting cold: their films lasted ten minutes each and covered the mother's first contact with her baby (except for the brief look at him immediately after delivery). From these films Klaus and Kennell made records of each child's movements, the position of his mother's fingertips and palms on his body, head, hands, and feet; the amount of time the mother spent smiling; the amount of time she spent either physically supporting or cradling him with her hands; and the amount of time the two of them spent *en face* (that is, with heads aligned so that they could look into one another's eyes).

The results of these observations showed that each mother went through an "orderly and predictable" pattern of behavior when she first examined her newborn infant. Beginning hesitantly with her fingertips, she touched his hands and feet and then within four or five minutes began to caress his body with the palms of her hands, showing increasing excitement as she did so. This examination continued for several minutes, and then diminished as the mother dozed off with the naked baby at her side. During the ten minutes of filming there was also a marked increase in the time that the mother positioned herself and her baby so that they could look into one another's eyes (if the baby had his eyes open). At the same time, she showed intense interest in waking her infant in an attempt to get him to open his eyes, and this was verbalized by nearly three quarters of the mothers: "Open your eyes, oh come on now, open your eyes," or "If you open your eyes I'll know you're alive." Several mothers also mentioned that, once the infant looked at them, they felt much closer to him.

Klaus and Kennell reviewed studies done on the behavior of

animals immediately after giving birth, and they think that the reactions described above are specific to human beings. They also speculate that, just as in the rhesus monkey, there are clear-cut patterns and orders of behavior—cradling, grooming, nursing, restraining, retrieving—that are components in establishing early affectional ties between animal mothers and their newborn offspring, so may this period immediately after birth also be especially sensitive for the development of affectional ties in human beings too.

My own observations of mothers and their babies differ in many ways from Klaus's and Kennell's because I was looking at the time in the delivery room immediately after birth, starting from the time the baby's head was delivered, through to his being given to his mother, sometimes to his father, and to the time he was taken away to be washed and weighed. In this situation the baby was well wrapped up, and the only exposed parts were the head and sometimes small pink hands and feet.

I recorded twelve deliveries, all of them in similar delivery rooms in a large maternity hospital. Some of them were in the consultant unit and attended by obstetricians, and some of them were in the general-practitioner unit in the same hospital. In the latter cases the delivery was performed by a midwife, usually well known to the mother, with the mother's practitioner standing by. In general it was a relatively short time between the delivery and the time the baby was given to the mother to hold: between 1 minute 25 seconds and 9 minutes, with an average for the group of about 3.5 minutes. This delay was the period in which the mouth was cleared and the baby was observed to make sure his breathing was all right. The baby was with the mother for an average of 6.5 minutes, but it varied between 1 minute and 15.5 minutes. When holding their babies, the mothers spent nearly three quarters of the time looking at them, and a third of that time smiling or laughing. Nine of the twelve mothers talked directly to their babies, and on an average all mothers spent about 80 percent of the time with both hands supporting or holding the baby, though again the variation was large—0 to 100 percent, in fact.

This is all rather dry information and conveys nothing of the emotional complexity, richness, and passion of what actually happens. Looking at and listening to my videotapes of deliver-

ies, certain marked differences as well as similarities showed up between the Klaus and Kennell study and my own. Although many of the mothers did start by touching the babies with their fingertips, few progressed to stroking with the palms of the hands and few manipulated the hands and feet. This progression was hampered in most cases because the baby was wrapped up, and there were also differences resulting from the procedures for delivering the placenta and from alterations in position and interruptions as episiotomies were sewn up.

But there were many other factors influencing behavior. There was, most obviously, the mother's individual personality and the way she reacted to the situation, unique in all aspects. There was the factor of what drugs she had been given to relieve pain; a drug like pethidine would interfere with her normal perception of the world. In other cases it was an epidural, which removed all sensation from the lower half of her body. Then, too, sometimes the father was present, sometimes not. Sometimes the mother might have seen the midwife throughout pregnancy and had the chance of forming a relaxed and trusting relationship; in other cases the mother was delivered by an obstetrician and nurses who were completely unknown, on duty for that particular day in the hospital. The expression of deep emotions within our society very much depends on social custom. Childbirth is perhaps the one time when it is always acceptable to show emotions, but this still strongly depends on who is present to see and hear them. If the father is there, or others who are well known, it is far more likely that the mother will openly demonstrate her feelings, be they joy, despondency, or anything else. The length of labor, the difficulty of the delivery, the sex of the child, and much more, all seem to play their part in influencing behavior in these first minutes.

What I find particularly fascinating is what the mothers say. Obviously the situation is in some ways beyond the bounds of convention, and there is no correct or incorrect thing to say or way to behave. Along with Klaus and Kennell, I noted the intense interest in the baby's eyes. Of course, the baby's eyes needed to be open, and with my deliveries this happened with only three of the twelve. Mrs. C in the transcript here does not actually greet the baby directly until he opens his eyes, and then says "Hello!" to him seven times in less than one and a half min-

utes. Just prior to this she has asked her baby to open his eyes.

There is also the parents' adjustment to the sex of their child, especially where they had strongly desired a child of the opposite sex. In Mrs. D's delivery the baby is held up for the father to see, who says "It's a boy" though in fact it's a girl. The midwife and the mother correct him, and he admits "I got my things sorted out wrong." They all then exchange bantering remarks about the fact that she won't be able to play rugby. I think that behind this banter there is a very serious grappling with the baby's being a girl, an adjustment that starts at this moment and probably takes a considerable time to complete.

In some of the transcripts the mother verbalizes her detailed initial examination of the child. Mrs. C goes over the baby, touching here and there with her fingers and remarking to her husband, "Look at his little mouth—Look at his little face—His little nails—His little squashed-up nose, like your nose—Look at his little head—Look at his hair." A sort of joyous, wondering inventory and, at the same time, a serious check to make sure that everything is there as it is meant to be.

Another fairly common thing among new mothers, which I have noted not only from this particular study but also from other deliveries I have watched, is for them to note how some feature of the baby's anatomy is just like the father's. Mrs. B says, "She's got your little tiny nose," and Mrs. C, "His little squashed-up nose, like your nose." In the case of Mrs. A it is the husband who likens the baby to himself, "It's nice, got my nose and my eyes." Although I would agree that frequently a combination of the baby's features may look like one parent's or the other's, it seems odd to point out any particular feature. The nose seems especially common, which again to me is strange since a baby's nose is actually very different from an adult's nose. It is usually the mother who likens the child to the father rather than the other way round, and I cannot help speculating whether this is the mother saying to the father, "Look, this really is *your* baby because it looks like you." After all, they both know it is her baby—she has just given birth.

A mother's first response to her baby is by no means always positive, and Kenneth Robson and Howard Moss, in a study of fifty-four women having their first babies, found that most women described some initial feelings of strangeness, distance,

and unfamiliarity toward their offspring, which persisted for at least the first few weeks of life.[2] Henry Kempe and his associates did a study that involved filming a very large number of mothers, in hospital delivery rooms, to see whether it was possible to predict from the mother's greeting her later relationship with the baby.[3] Some of the mothers showed distinct distaste and disgust as the baby was presented to them, and by scoring certain aspects of maternal behavior at this time Kempe did find that he could tell whether the mother would have a hard time forming normal relationships with her child later.

THE BABY'S EXPERIENCE

Most of us have no memory of our own births but, as John Davies said, this "does not mean that the experience is lost or is not having any influence." There are those who have reexperienced their birth by the use of drugs or hypnosis, and many have found the experience to be unpleasant, even traumatic. There are other ways for us to try and estimate what the experience is for the baby. We can as adults imagine what it's like to be squeezed through a narrow tube, which is warm, dark, wet, and only slightly yielding, for several hours. We can also observe the baby, during or just after birth, to see whether the experience he has just undergone seemed traumatic. There is the possibility that during delivery itself the baby is only semiconscious. Before birth the fetus is sensitive to touch: when a needle is put into the amniotic fluid (through the mother's abdominal and uterine wall, using local anesthetic) and touches the baby itself, the baby tries to move the touched part away from the needle. This may well be a reflex, and the baby may not be conscious of either the needle or the movement. Observations make it clear, though, that a baby can feel pain immediately after delivery and, unless one proposes some very delicate switch to turn on sensitivity to pain only after birth, it seems reasonable to assume that the infant is also capable of feeling pain during birth.

Immediately after a spontaneous delivery, where the mother has received no drugs and there were no other complications, the baby is often remarkably alert. After the first unique cry, expanding the lungs that have till now been filled with fluid, the child will, if kept warm and handled gently, lie quietly with his

eyes open and looking around. If you move your face very slowly backward and forward about nine inches away from his, he may follow you with jerky, uncoordinated eye movements. Another reported observation is that if a clicking noise is made close to one ear and then to the other, he will tend to turn his eyes toward the click.[4] So probably the baby not only can see and hear but can also make attempts to determine which of two sides a sound is coming from and to keep a stimulating sight within the field of vision.

The French obstetrician Frederick Leboyer, from his extensive experience of watching childbirth, feels in no uncertain terms that the processes of birth are agony for the child: "Hell exists, and is white hot. It is not a fable. But we go through it at the beginning of our lives, not the end. Hell is what the child goes through to reach us. Its flames assail the child from every side; they burn its eyes, its skin, they sear its flesh; they devour. This fire is what the baby feels as the air rushes into the lungs. The air, which enters and sweeps through the trachea, and expands the alveoli, is like acid poured on a wound."[5] A powerful description. For my part, after watching babies very closely after delivery, I am surprised at how untraumatized they seem to be. Frequently after the first loud cry, the baby quiets down rapidly and lies still, apparently content to try and come to terms with his new surroundings. There is no way of actually knowing, of course—we can only surmise.

Leboyer, quite correctly, points out that we know the newborn infant can see, hear, and is exquisitely sensitive to his surroundings. The baby should therefore be treated and respected as a real person, who is having to make a very rapid adaptation from the only familiar environment he has known—the semidark, rhythmically noisy, water-suspended, warm and pulsating squeezing world of the uterus—to a sudden blast of noise, light, cold, and air. During this same period the baby's method of getting oxygen completely changes; instead of being transmitted from the blood of the mother across the placenta to the baby's blood, it has to come from the baby's own lungs, and this involves huge changes in the circulation of blood through his body.

To help the baby make these changes a little less rapidly, giving him more time to adapt, Leboyer suggests that, after the

head has been delivered, the lights in the room should be dimmed and everyone should remain silent or at least talk in whispers. Then, when the rest of the delivery has taken place, and before the cord is cut, the baby should be placed immediately on the mother's tummy so that he can again feel direct contact with her. This will also help to keep the baby warm and perhaps, with one ear against the abdominal wall, reassured by hearing the rhythmical thud of the maternal heartbeat. At this stage, Leboyer feels, everyone must learn to wait. The cord should not be cut immediately but should be allowed to undergo the normal physiological changes that close off the blood supply from the placenta as the baby makes his first attempts at breathing. During this time he encourages the mother to massage her baby, to get to know what he feels like and to allow him gradually to become aware of what she feels like, externally. Later the doctor immerses the child in warm water, returning him to the weightlessness of the uterus.

Leboyer does not make scientific claims but simply says "Look and see for yourself." If his ideas become widely adopted, it will not be because of their scientific rightness or wrongness, but because our society wants to accept them at this particular moment in time. I think that Leboyer will be accepted, even though I also think that delivering a baby into complete silence when he has been surrounded by rhythmical sound might be terrifying. In fact, when the child is born, he still has fluid in the middle ear, which dampens noises until the fluid is absorbed over the first week. As a pediatrician I also wonder about the dangers of putting the child into water immediately after birth. The baby's ability to control his temperature is exceedingly poor at this stage, and keeping babies warm has been one of the real advances in reducing infant deaths in this period after birth. Still, none of these things should detract from the basic premise that the child is born a sensitive human being and needs to be treated as such.

THE FATHER'S PRESENCE

In our society the role of the father in childbirth is confused and ambiguous. In certain cultures he may have a well-defined and ritualized part to play, even in some tribes going through the pains of labor and delivery surrounded by sympathetic friends

and relatives, while his wife has been sent outside the village to have the baby in isolation. In other cultures a man may be totally excluded from playing any part in the birth of his own child.

In Britain and the United States, with the advent of modern obstetrics, fathers were initially excluded from the hospital delivery room, on the grounds that they had no active medical part to play in life saving and were therefore an unhygienic, superfluous accessory who might get in the way of the specialist. As better social conditions have made childbirth safer and the death of the mother or baby has become less likely, the majority of births take place without mishap, thereby shifting the emphasis from mere physical survival to the emotional well-being of those concerned. Fathers are by no means always kept from the delivery room now.

It is easy to see how fathers may still feel excluded from the birth, even though actually present. Many prenatal clinics and programs have made an effort to involve the father actively, by teaching him how to help and support the mother during labor and delivery. The Charing Cross Hospital in London, for instance, a few years ago ran a program to teach husbands how to become more active participants in the labor. Of the first 730 husbands taking part, 61 percent were present throughout the whole of labor and 39 percent were present for part of it; 75 percent saw the baby being delivered and 99.6 percent said they were glad to be there; 92 percent thought their presence was beneficial. It is interesting to note that the social class of the men taking part in the study showed a strong bias toward the upper end.

Encouragement for fathers to be present during birth has only come in the last decade, and there are many places that still exclude them. Part of the reason has to do with the changing mechanics of technical obstetrics. In a recent study of induction, a random selection of one hundred mothers showed that fathers were present in only 18 percent of births, less than one in five. Closer analysis showed that more fathers were present in the noninduced control group than in the induced groups, and that the incidence of epidurals and forceps deliveries was also much higher in the induced groups. At the hospital where the study was done, it was the practice to move mothers from the normal delivery room to the operating theater if they needed forceps,

and in general the fathers were excluded from the theater. So obstetrics, having reached the point of accepting the presence of fathers during delivery, altered its procedures and excluded them again.

In my study of the twelve deliveries, the father was present in six, and held the baby in three. The mothers spent about half as much time smiling at their husbands as they did at their newborn babies. From superficial observation of the videotapes, the husbands demonstrated great variation in the amount of direct support they showed their wives. But support can be given in many ways, and most of them are probably invisible to the camera. A study by W. J. Henneborn and R. Cogan showed that, when husbands attended special classes prior to birth and were present during delivery, this had a positive effect on their wives' reported feelings of pain, and decreased the use of medication.[6] It also markedly altered the couples' hindsight of the birth experience. In an unpublished study S. Tanzer compared deliveries where the husband was or was not present during the second stage of labor. Her findings show a striking effect of the husband's presence upon the wife's birth experience. In every case in which the women reported "raptures" and a "peak" of experience during birth, her husband had been with her in the delivery room.

There is an attempt today to break down the specific roles of men and women so that these roles can become interchangeable. Pregnancy, labor, and delivery will remain with the woman, should she want them, but it is not impossible to imagine that a man who is involved in helping his wife throughout pregnancy and labor, and who is present at delivery, shares in the moment, holds the child, and is immediately involved in the day-to-day routines of child care, will find it easier to continue this role later. A study from Sweden seems to support this idea.[7] Soon after their wives had delivered, a group of fathers went to the hospital twice to handle their babies and change their diapers. Follow-up at home showed that these fathers later spent more time with their infants than a control group of father who did not have this early experience.

There has been extensive research on the effects of childbirth on early mother-child relationships, but much remains to be learned about the early relationship of father and child, and also of father and mother.

TRANSCRIPT: MRS. B, AGED 27, FIRST BABY (A GIRL)

Father	Mother	Doctor
		Come on, junior. Only a lady could cause so much trouble. Come on, little one.
	(baby is delivered)	
	A girl.	
		Well, it's got the right plumbing.
	Oh I'm sorry, darling.	
(laughs)		
		What are you sorry about?
	He wanted a boy.	
		Well, you'll have to try again next week, won't you!
	(laughs)	
		She looks great. Want to see her? Bloody and messy, but that's not from her.
	Oh, she's gorgeous.	
	(mother kisses father)	
Looks like you.		
		Sorry, dear, I'm just going to need your cooperation for a moment. Will you move your

Father	Mother	Doctor
		bottom down the bed towards me—you've crept up the bed rather.
	Sorry. Do you want me to push?	
		Again please. No. A little more of your bottom down the bed.
	She's big, isn't she?	
		She's no Twiggy, this one.
	Seven pounds three you guessed.	
		Yes. I think I may have been a bit conservative.
	What do you think she is?	
		She's a bit more than that, I think.
	Oh darling, how do you feel?	
		Relax your thighs, ma'am.
	(laughs)	
		Give me a cough.
	(coughs)	
	I'll stand on my head if you want me to now.	
		Not at all, dear.
Ooh!		

(whispers to husband)

We've had to make a little cut, as we often do, but I don't think you'll feel it, and I'll just stitch that up right away. Do you feel it?

Yes.

It's just the afterbirth now.

Is she all right?

Why don't you ask her? She's quite capable of letting you know how she feels about the situation.

She's noisy, isn't she?

Yes, just like the modern generation.

Well, Dr. Murphy, I was right. I had a sneaky feeling it was a girl, just because I wanted a boy.

(laughs)

Yes.

Well, it will suit your mum, won't it?

Often tactically best to have a girl first—she can help with the washing up.

Father	Mother	Doctor
	(baby given to mother)	
	Hello darling. Meet your dad. You're just like your dad *(baby yells)*.	
I'm going home!	Oh you've gone quiet *(laughs)*. Oh darling, she's just like you—she's got your little tiny nose.	
It'll grow like yours.	She's big, isn't she? What do you reckon?	She's quite good-looking, despite forceps marks on her head— but don't worry about that. She'll have little bruises around her ears—well, they usually have. I don't know if she does.
	There's one—there . . . Oh look, she's got hair. It's a girl—you're supposed to be all little.	What do you think she weighs, Richard? I think about seven and a half.

Gosh. Oh, she's lovely. Oh, she's opened her eyes (*laughs*). Oh lovely (*kisses baby*).

She's a little bit bloody and messy, but that's from where I made the cut to help her out, and none of it's from her, so no need for concern.

Oh, she's gorgeous, she's lovely. She's got blue eyes. You hold her. Come on.

No.

Why not? (*laughs*) You're all of a tremble, aren't you?

I dropped the first one I held.

Charming!

Oh look, oh mine. Hello darling. Good lungs, hasn't she? She's got a dimple—where'd she get that from?

That's probably from the forceps. Actually, have you got dimples?

Doctor	Mother	Father
	Oh no, neither of us have. Oh, you're lovely. Look . . . . She's lovely. I thought she'd be all mauve and crinkly.	
Oh, she's in great nick.		
	Yes. I was expecting her to be all mauve and shrivelled, but she's not, is she?	
Not at all. In front of the cameras she's a real lady.		
	Oh dear. Having your photo taken, darling? Oh.	
Ma'am, can I ask you to drop your ankles apart?		
	She doesn't go much on this (nurse attaching name-tag to baby).	
		Like British Rail, labelling her like a parcel.
	Oh look, darling, look at the size of her feet. She's got no toenails.	
What do you mean, she hasn't got any toenails?		

She hasn't got any toenails. They're soft.

I don't think you'd like it if she was scratching around inside you.

Look—fabulous. Aren't you pleased with her?

Yes, of course.

I'm not putting her back.

You said that if it was a girl it could go back.

Back to the manufacturers, yes.

Well, it came from him in the first place.

It's his spermatozoa that decides the sex.

Quite. (*kisses the baby and laughs*)

I shall be worried to death when she's eighteen.

You'll imagine her going out with all sorts of blokes like you were. (*laughs*) In a sort of odd way I was after his money really.

Yes?

All two quid. Go, go to dad.

Father	Mother	Doctor
		Come on, the generation gap can't be showing so soon.
No, she doesn't want to.		
	Yes she does.	
No she doesn't.		
	Go on, cuddle her, she won't bite you. Don't be silly, of course she won't.	
Are you sure?		
	Yes, go on—she won't hurt.	
I don't know how it's done.		
	(baby given to father)	
	It doesn't really matter. They're built like rubber anyway at that stage.	
Well, she's not cleaned yet.		
	She's a bit yukky and revolting, but she's rather sweet. It's a jolly good job they do. I suppose you've decided that's what you always wanted to do in the first place. Why?	
	(baby given back to mother)	

Oh, you're lovely. Well, what do you think, love? Can you see her? Oh, she has got a long neck. You look as though you feel exhausted.

(*father jokingly handed gas by doctor*)

Quick whiff. I know what you want and that is a fag.

Haven't you been able to have one?

Yes. Yes. Well, painful, but I don't particularly care at this stage. She's opened her eyes. They're not—they're dark blue. Don't say they're brown— we haven't got brown eyes in either family.

(*laughs*) It's not gas I want, It's a triple brandy.

Oh dear, fancy wanting a nice fag.

Sorry, ma'am, I'm putting needles in a part where you're not numb. Am I hurting you?

Father	Mother	Doctor
		They're always blue in the beginning and find their own colour later.
		Plastic surgery of the first order.
	God, it doesn't . . . Doing a lovely piece of darning down there?	
	How splendid. Well, if you look in the book case at home, in the right hand book case, hidden behind the bible is a bottle of Tia Maria.	
		Behind the bible!
	It's the place he wouldn't look. Oh dear.	
		I'm sorry.

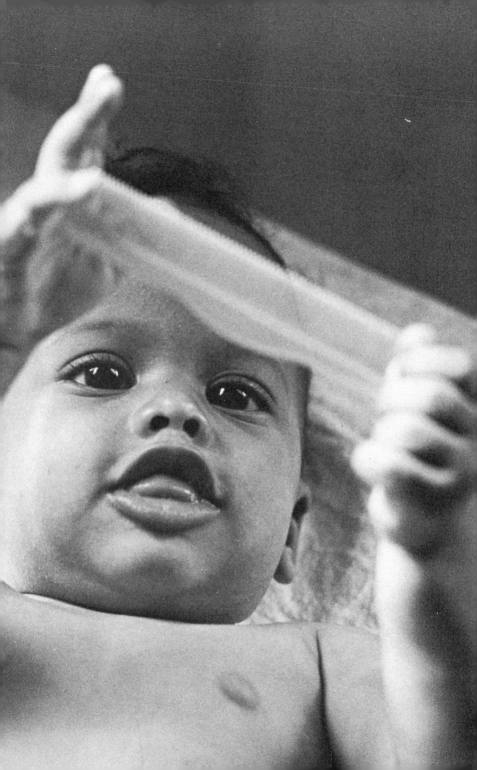

6 / What the Baby Knows

It has come as more of a surprise to psychologists than to mothers (though the two of course are not mutually exclusive) that babies, after nine months of development in the uterus, are born so highly organized. They are born with a great number of automatic reflexes, performed in response to appropriate stimulation: they grasp objects put in the palm of their hands; they attempt to crawl if put face downward on a firm surface; they extend and flex their arms rapidly if their heads are let drop a short distance; they purse their lips if the base of the thumb is lighly stroked; they curve their backs when scratched down one side of the spine; they make stepping movements with the foot if the back of the foot is firmly stroked with the leg is extended; they turn their heads when the side of the mouth is touched. They are also able to select and use a great deal of information from their surroundings, and they show a wide range of behavior to demonstrate their needs in both subtle and forceful ways.

At one time it was thought that a newborn baby received all sensations from the environment, with no selectivity or discrimination. But this is not so, not by far. Although we are still discovering just how competent the newborn baby is, it is obvious that, just by being born human, the infant fresh out from his mother's womb already has the ability to be attracted to the features of another human being. This is remarkable because he has had no previous experience of the sight or sound of human beings from the outside.

How do we know what babies can see, hear, or feel? How can we tell that they are more attracted to one thing than to another, when they are so tiny? There are many ways of finding out,

73

some more complicated than others. We might simply watch the baby and carefully note all the things he does in a fifteen-second period in every minute for an hour, or we might record the baby's heartbeat and breathing rhythm to see if they change when something happens to the baby. We might also build a highly complicated piece of machinery which, say, shines a light into the baby's eyes so that it reflects from the backs of the eyes into a television camera; this produces a picture on a screen which can be automatically analyzed by computer to show what exactly the baby is looking at. These are just a few examples of how observations are made, but undoubtedly the most pleasant is that used by mothers when trying to find out what their babies are thinking—watching them very carefully. One of the masters at baby watching is Peter Wolff. He studied a group of ten babies in their own homes, each for thirty hours per week.[1] He was particularly interested in the amount of time the babies spent in an attentive state, when they have "a general disposition to respond adaptively to selected elements in a constantly changing environment." In this state the baby is fully awake, breathing evenly, with eyes wide open, and quiet. The time he spends like this increases over the weeks, from 11 percent in the first week to 21 percent by the fourth. The rest of the time he is either drowsy, asleep, or crying. Wolff also observed that with this group of infants, during the first six hours immediately after birth the amount of alert inactivity varied greatly from infant to infant: some stayed awake for an hour and a half before the first sleep and did not have another alert period of equal length until the end of the first month; others fell asleep within fifteen minutes of delivery and would only wake up fully on the second or third day.

The reason I mention this here is that a baby's reactions to the changing environment greatly depend on the state he is in. It is common now, when making observations, to divide the baby's degree of "awakeness" into six possible categories: (1) deep sleep, with regular breathing, (2) light sleep, with irregular breathing and occasional restlessness, (3) drowsy, (4) awake, eyes open, but quiet rather than excited, (5) awake, eyes open, but moving actively, and (6) crying. (Some researchers use only five categories, dividing [3] between [2] and [4].[2])

The best time to observe the baby's reactions to different

sights, sounds, and smells is when he is alert, in state 4. Unfortunately, as Wolff's study suggests, the time the baby spends like this in the first few days is very short. There are ways to improve our chances for good observation, however. First we can observe the babies at certain times of day, since there is evidence that babies spend more time alert just before or after feeds. This is not always true, though; just before a feeding the baby may be too hungry and start crying if not fed immediately. After a feeding he may drop off to sleep. The extent of this period of alertness seems to depend as well on whether the babies are being demand-fed or schedule-fed. If we choose to observe a baby just before he is fed, we can stop him from crying and keep him in an apparently alert state by getting him to suck on a blind teat. But the very act of sucking in itself alters the way in which he reacts to the environment, since babies have difficulty in dividing their attention between two things—for instance, between sucking and looking. Paul Harris and I did a study to see how far sideways a baby would look if we presented him with a flashing light nine inches away and starting in the periphery of his vision. The degree to which babies responded was much greater if they were not sucking.[3]

For many tests the best time is between meals, when babies are not yet hungry for their next meal. At this time a baby is usually sleeping, and he has to be waked up with great gentleness and care, by talking to him, very slowly turning him over, hesitantly removing his clothing, and so on; as much or even more care is needed to keep him in an alert state once he is awake. All those who try and observe the baby's reactions to different specific things know the patience needed and the frustrations involved.

Many other factors affect a baby's state of alertness. Heinz Prechtl gathered evidence from the brain-wave patterns of very small babies that they were never fully awake under two weeks of age if they were lying flat on their backs, but were much more alert if they were lying at an angle, with their heads higher than their feet, or were fully upright.[4] We probably all have noticed how alert babies seem when they are held up against the shoulder, and during breastfeeding the head is held higher than the legs. Originally, many psychologists did test babies when they were flat on their backs, and got negative results. But in some cases, when they repeated the tests with the babies sitting up, the

babies responded, and today we frequently use small supportive chairs, inclined at an angle, for babies to sit in. Other factors affecting response include the temperature of the surroundings: too hot and the baby goes off to sleep, too cold and he starts crying. Touch also matters: if the baby is tightly swaddled, he tends to go to sleep, but he may become distressed if totally naked. Light is an influence: too much and he shuts his eyes with a grimace, too dim and he may go to sleep again.

If the baby is to respond to certain things in the outside world he needs to encounter certain features or stimuli that attract his attention, and he has to link them up to his previous experiences. If the stimulus is too intense, too bright, too noisy, or has too many novel features, then he may defend himself—show withdrawal behavior such as turning away or crying. If the intensity of the stimulus is too low or too familiar, then he may ignore it. These changes of behavior seem to be accompanied by changes in heartrate. If the baby is interested and attentive to an event, then his heartbeat tends to slow down. If the stimulus is too intense or frightening, then his heart speeds up, perhaps in preparation for defense of some sort.

SEEING

It is quite easy to observe that the newborn baby can appreciate brightness and that he does not like very bright lights. Even with the eyes closed and when he is asleep, he will screw up his eyes, frown, and tense his muscles if a bright light is suddenly shone directly into his face. If, however, he is awake and is brought near a window, provided he is not directly in sunlight he will often turn toward the light, indicating that he knows where it is and is attracted by it. It would seem possible that if one shone a bright light on the pregnant mother's tummy sometime before delivery, the baby might turn toward it, and perhaps some of the baby's movements before birth stem from this.

But after he is born, a baby is very much more discriminating. If you move your head slowly backward and forward nine inches away from his face, he may follow it for short distances, with jerky eye movements. To discover which features of the human face a baby preferred to look at, Robert Fantz showed a series of babies three flat objects, all in the size and shape of a

head.[5] On the first was painted a regular stylized face in black on a pink background. The second had the same features as the first, but scrambled, and on the third was painted a solid black patch at one end, equal in area to the features of the first two. The babies he tested were aged from four days old to six months, but the results showed that, at all ages, they looked most at the real face, somewhat less at the scrambled face, and least at the third object with the black patch.

Most of the studies on what babies prefer to look at have involved presenting them with two things at the same time and observing their eye movements to see which one they look at more. This method has shown that babies are attracted by contrast. They like complex patterns in which there is a great deal of sharp demarcation. It is therefore not surprising that they are found to watch particularly the eyes of the human face, for with their whites, darker irises, and black pupils, the eyes present definite contrasts. It is obviously interesting and significant that infants should be attracted to eyes and faces as they are.

Preference studies of this sort have also been used to judge how good a baby's eyesight is.[6] Since a baby prefers looking at contours or contrast rather than at, say, a gray field, one can present him with pairs of cards, each showing black and white lines of equal width. On successive different cards for comparison, the black and white lines grow narrower and narrower. At a certain point one card will appear to the baby as an all-gray blur, when the lines are so narrow that they cannot be seen individually. When this happens the baby will show a preference for the other, whose slightly wider lines he can see clearly. This point seems to be reached at cards with lines one eighth of an inch wide.

It was not realized until recently that very small babies could see at all, because it had not been discovered that they have a fairly rigid distance of focus, at somewhere around nine inches. If you want a baby to look at something, it is best to show it to him at this distance—which is incidentally just about the same distance the mother's face is from her baby's when she is breastfeeding. Recent work shows that this distance may not be completely fixed, for by examining the movements of each eye individually, and the distance between the center of the pupils, we can observe that the eyes converge and diverge when babies

look at objects ten to twenty inches away, but that they don't when the objects are nearer or farther off.[7] This strongly suggests that babies do see objects within this range, but not outside it. (This effect of convergence is exactly what happens if you watch a finger moving toward or away from your nose.) In the study mentioned, the eye movements were analyzed from film. If, however, we observe the baby's eyes directly, with no special technique, convergence can't be detected before the child is twenty weeks old.

Tom Bower wanted to measure the newborn baby's expectation that an object would be solid.[8] He filmed the reactions of a series of babies, aged less than two weeks, while a large object was moved at different speeds toward them. Examining the films he found that, as the object approached, the babies pulled their heads back and put their hands between them and the object. This shows that they already have a reaction that would defend them against getting hit by the object, and implies that they expect it to be solid. The reaction was specific for objects approaching at a certain speed and on a "hit path," for if the object moved away from or to one side of the baby, or if the speed of approach changed, then he did not react. Another experiment that Bower did was to create the optical illusion of an object by using polaroid light. If the baby was sitting up in a special supportive chair so that his arms and hands were free to move, he appeared to try and grasp an object if it was presented as within reach. If it was an illusory object and he tried to grasp it only to find that it wasn't there, he was greatly disturbed. This, then, seems to indicate that at least one aspect of the coordination between eye and hand is present at birth. The baby expects to feel what he can see.

The most common of the more complicated sights a baby sees after birth is his mother's face, not as a still object in one plane, like a photograph, but as a dynamic and continually moving object with varied expressions and different associated contexts, such as food and warmth. How soon does the baby come to distinguish his mother's face from others? Genevieve Carpenter sat two-week-old babies in supportive chairs and, when they were alert, presented them with either their mother's face or a strange mother's face in an opening in a frame in front of them.[9] She observed the babies' general behavior, where they looked and

for how long. At two weeks the babies spent a longer time looking at their own mother's face than they did at the stranger's
face. In fact, when they were presented with the strange mother's
face, they frequently showed strong gaze aversion, looking right
away almost over their shoulders. This kind of withdrawal suggests that the babies found the stimulus too intense or too novel.

HEARING

It is obvious to most mothers that their babies can hear. If the
baby is alert, then a loud noise, such as a door slamming, will
usually make him tense up or startle. However, we should
remember that during the first few days after birth the middle
part of the ear behind the eardrum is still full of amniotic fluid,
and that this only gradually gets absorbed or evaporates. Until it
is, sounds reaching the baby's ear are dampened.

I have already mentioned a study by Michael Wertheimer,
who sounded clicks at one or other of a newborn's ears and noted
that he turned his eyes toward the clicks.[10] At four days of age
or even younger, a baby can be taught to turn his head one way
for a bell and the other way for a buzzer, by rewarding him
when he is right. But there is a great deal more that we know
about the baby's hearing. Recently there has been considerable
work done on the response to sound inside the uterus very early
in labor. This has been made possible by putting a very small
microphone on the end of a catheter and inserting it into the
uterus after the membranes have broken; it is placed close to the
baby's ear and can record the noise actually reaching him. Since
it is possible as well to record his heartrate at this stage, we can
produce a loud noise at the mother's tummy wall, and both
record it from inside the uterus and see what effects it has on the
heartrate. It seems from this, and from work done with babies
right after birth, that "patterned" sounds produce more response
than pure tones, and that the most effective sound of all is one
that includes the fundamental frequencies found in the human
voice. There is also evidence from research done by John Hutt
that babies respond better to the higher frequencies.[11] In the light
of this, it is interesting that both mothers and fathers often talk
to their babies in high-pitched voices but return to normal as
soon as they talk to another adult again. It is also true that if

one holds a baby up and has a man talk to it normally from one side and a woman from the other, the baby seems to turn more frequently to the woman. If the woman is the mother, it seems as if the baby is actually recognizing her. And this may in fact be so, for another study shows that if a mother consistently calls her baby by name every time she picks him up, or feeds him or is near him, then by the third day, if she stands out of the baby's line of sight and calls his name, he will frequently turn toward her. If a strange mother does the same thing, the baby is much less likely to respond.

A more controlled study of this kind was done by Margaret Mills.[12] She tested babies who were between twenty and thirty days of age, and arranged things so that when they sucked on a teat, they heard a recording of either their own mother's or a strange mother's voice, both matched for loudness. She found that the babies would suck significantly more to conjure up the sound of their own mother. So this is another subtle difference in babies' behavior toward mothers and strangers.

I have already talked about the baby's ability to tell whether a sound comes from the right or the left, as indicated by eye movements. It is suggested that one way that he can tell which side a sound is coming from is because the sound waves reach one ear before the other, and because different parts of the waves reach the two ears. In order to locate a sound, a baby might turn his head so that the sound reaching the two ears is equal. This is all somewhat confused by some studies which suggest that the two ears do not appreciate sound equally: quiet sounds played at the left ear do not affect the direction of the eye movements as much as they do if played at the right ear, and it is therefore possible that the two ears may have different thresholds of sensitivity.[13]

Turning the eyes toward a sound is certainly quite sophisticated, but five-day-old babies seem to be able to do even better than this. If instead of eye-turning we look at the baby's patterns of head-turning, we find that to a certain extent he seems to be able to tell from what angle a sound is coming. For instance, babies will turn their heads more toward a sound coming from an angle of 80 degrees from the midline than toward a sound coming from 15 degrees from the midline on the same side.

It also seems that if you turn your face backward and forward in front of the baby's face without talking, he tends to follow

you with jerky eye movements, and only starts making head movements when his eyes can no longer continue the tracking by themselves. If, however, you talk to him at the same time, head movements seem to begin almost simultaneously with the eye movements—as if he were trying to keep the sound coming from a position between his two ears. Occasionally I have observed babies who under these conditions make no eye movements at all, but simply track the face by holding the eyes straight ahead and moving the head only.

Finally there are the intriguing findings of William Condon, who for many years analyzed films of adults talking to one another. He found that people talking seemed to move in synchrony with speech. This "dance" can only be detected by careful film analysis, when even the very smallest movements can be examined. Condon and Louis Sander later joined in a project of videotaping a series of infants aged between twelve hours and two days old, and they showed that even at this incredibly early age the babies seem to move in precise time to human speech. They did so whether the speech they heard was in English or Chinese.[14]

SMELL

Smell is another of the senses by which we gather information about other people and the world around. Our sense of smell is not particularly good when compared with many animals, but we are nevertheless capable of considerable discrimination between smells, and many of us find smells very evocative. It seems that smell is a fairly old sense in terms of our evolutionary development and is associated with parts of the brain which are themselves phylogenetically ancient.

We all have body smells (a fact some of us consider unfortunate) which are as unique to us as our fingerprints. Related people have related smells. Bloodhounds know this, for a hound after sniffing a man is more likely to follow the track of that man's brother than of some stranger. It is also possible that we emit subtle smells that influence the behavior of others, without any of us knowing it. For instance, the fact that women living in the same institution after a while come to menstruate at the same time may be due to the influence of smells, and the smell of a

woman during ovulation may have strange effects on the concentration of men around here. It is also significant that we tend to use smells more during close body contact, as when making love, and this may well be true during the course of early mother-baby contact.

That very small babies can smell has been shown by Engen, Lipsitt, and Kay, who observed the activity, heartrate, and breathing patterns of twenty babies aged two days.[15] Each baby was presented with two smells chosen from anise oil, asafetida, acetic acid, or phenyl alcohol. When a smell was initially presented to the baby, he changed his activity, heartrate, and breathing patterns. If the smell continued, the baby gradually learned to take no notice of it (habituation), but as soon as the smell was changed to a new one, then up went the activity and heartrate and breathing patterns changed again—the infant recognized the smell as being different from the one he had become used to.

Recently I have done several studies with small babies to test just how sensitive their sense of smell is.[16] I had noticed that sometimes when a baby is put to his mother's breast, he turns his face to the breast even before he has looked at it or before his face has been touched by the nipple. This might have been due to his sensing the heat of the breast, and indeed infra-red photographs show that the two breasts and the lips of a lactating woman are her warmest areas of skin. It might also be that the baby learns very rapidly that when one side of his body is held against his mother he has to turn his head to that side to get fed. However, the baby might also be smelling the breast, for each time the baby is fed he will have his nose in close contact with the breast, so that the food and the smell may become closely associated.

What I did initially was to take a breast pad (a piece of gauze measuring four inches square) which had been inside the mother's bra between feeds, and put it at one side of the baby's head, touching his cheek. At the same time, I put a clean breast pad on the other side against the cheek and for one minute filmed all the movements of the baby's head; at the end of the minute I reversed the pads for another minute. Several previous studies had shown that babies tend spontaneously to turn their heads more to the right than the left, perhaps because mothers tend to put

their babies more often on their own left. Analysis of the films showed that at five days of age the babies were spending more time with their heads turned toward their mother's pad than to the clean pad. To get more subtle results I repeated the test but used another mother's breast pad instead of a clean one. At two days of age the babies spent an equal amount of time with both pads; but at six days the babies were generally spending more time turned to their own mother's pad than to the strange mother's pad. At ten days of age this effect was even more striking. All the babies were being breast-fed and were tested when they were most hungry, that is, just before a feeding. This still left open the question of whether it was the breast milk itself, the mother's smell, or a combination of the two that attracted the baby. So I did one further experiment, which revealed that babies do not turn toward breast milk on its own—perhaps the smell of the milk is not strong enough. Here again we witness the ability of the baby to distinguish his own mother from strange mothers at only six days of age. But frequently, when I told mothers I was doing a study to see if their babies could smell them, they rushed off, saying they must put on some deodorant. It was all I could do to dissuade them.

Perhaps smell also has an effect on the mother's behavior. In a pilot study we got a series of mothers to sniff their babies. We blindfolded the mothers and got them to wear earphones so they could neither see nor hear their babies. If they were given a choice of two babies to smell, a significant number managed to identify their own, though I suspect they may have been using other clues. Other observations related to smell are that babies who have been breast-fed and then changed to a bottle change their smell; this is probably due to an alteration in the smell of their excreta—the breast-fed baby's excreta are rather sweet-smelling, whereas the bottle-fed's are more like an adult's. It also seems that mothers become well adapted to the smell of their own baby's excreta but get nauseated at other babies'.

TASTE AND THE BREAST-BOTTLE ARGUMENT

Taste on its own is a relatively simple sense in human beings, and the finer discriminations that we think we can make by taste we actually make by smell.

There are two observations that indicate that the baby inside the uterus is able to taste. In the first chapter I described how the baby surrounded by fluid swallows it continually and then pees it out again, and there is evidence that the baby may actually control the amount of fluid around him. In certain pregnancies too much fluid sometimes accumulates too fast, and forty years ago a doctor developed a novel way of treating this. He injected saccharine into the amniotic fluid in order to sweeten it, and he found that he could thereby reduce the amount of fluid, possibly by having encouraged the baby to swallow more. More recently another doctor found that injecting a substance opaque to X-rays into the amniotic fluid caused a decrease in swallowing; this was clear from the X-ray pictures of the substance being swallowed by the child. The opaque substance he had injected was known to have an extremely unpleasant taste. All this suggests that a fetus can taste.

Louis Lipsitt and his colleagues have been looking at the effect of altering the sweetness of a feed on the baby's sucking patterns and on his heartrate.[17] Taking babies two to three days old, they arranged a system by which, each time the baby sucked, he got a minute fixed amount of fluid. This fluid contained varying amounts of sugar. They found that the more sugar there was in the solution, the slower the baby sucked and the more the heartrate increased. This is in some ways not what one would expect: certainly I would have thought that if the baby tasted a sweet substance he would have sucked faster to try and get more. In this case, however, where the baby was getting only a very small and fixed amount with each suck, he sucked more slowly; this should mean that less effort was used and the heart should have slowed down, but it did not—which is all very paradoxical. One explanation that Lipsitt put forward is that the sucking rate is slowed to make it easier for the baby to savor the sweeter fluid, and that perhaps the excitement of tasting a different and more concentrated fluid increases the heartrate. It is probable, though, that it is all more complicated than this.

Fascinating too are the results of work done by David Salisbury.[18] He was looking at the effects of different feeds on babies' swallowing, sucking, and breathing patterns. Previous work had shown that water, cow's milk, and glucose, when introduced into the back of a calf's throat, interrupted its breathing, while a

salt-water solution did not; this suggested that a calf has specialized taste receptors to prevent it from breathing when swallowing. Salisbury looked at the effects of feeding different solutions to human babies, and he found that, when given salt water, they suppressed breathing very poorly. When he fed them sterile water, however, none inhaled it—which suggests that a baby may also have these specialized taste receptors. Using a specially designed bottle, Salisbury also examined the breathing, sucking, and swallowing patterns of the infants when fed artificial milk or breast milk. Again the patterns were different for the two types.

It is known that the composition of breast milk alters as to the time of day and as to how far through a feeding the baby is. At the beginning breast milk is rather diluted; it becomes more concentrated toward the end. So the baby gets his fluids at the beginning and his food at the end. Shifting from one breast to another has been likened to having a drink in the middle of a meal.

The issue of breast- versus bottle-feeding, like those of induction and home delivery, has been highly contentious, because it highlights the economic, cultural, social, psychological, and physiological influences at work on human behavior. On the simplest level, human breast milk is produced by humans for humans and has developed over the course of human existence; it contains certain substances, and not others, for purposes we are only just becoming aware of. Most mothers can breastfeed given the right chance, and a small number cannot.

Breastfeeding is associated with a lower incidence of intestinal infection in the baby, a lower incidence of milk allergies, better protection against certain diseases, owing to the transfer of antibodies from the mother through her milk, and better protection against malnutrition or overfeeding, which can occur with artificial feeds. There is also evidence that the incidence of crib death is lower among breast-fed babies. As suggested by Salisbury's study, the incidence of inhalation of feeds into the lungs should be negligible on breast milk but might occur with artificial feeds if they contained certain concentrations of salt.

Psychological reasons for breastfeeding include the satisfaction that the mother might get from feeling that she is continuing to support and nourish the child from her own body. Her baby

will be held so that his face is nine inches away from hers, and as a result of his inclined position he will probably be fairly alert. The baby is also more likely to be held right up against the mother's body during the feeding.

Factors affecting the success or failure of breastfeeding have been suggested by Martin Richards and Judy Bernal.[19] They found that breast-fed babies seemed to cry more than those fed by bottle. The mothers in their study had been advised by medical personnel to feed their babies every four hours, although it is thought that the amount of protein in breast milk may only be enough to keep a baby from hunger for three hours. In response to their babies' cries, one group of mothers tended to give up, believing they could not produce enough milk. A second group continued to breastfeed, but fed more often. Interestingly, the first group of mothers tended to come from a lower social class than the second group, and the investigators suggested that the mothers who gave up were more responsive to the specific instruction they had received from the doctor, midwife, or nurse; the others had chosen to ignore this advice in the light of their own experience that feeding the baby more often stopped him from getting hungry.

The cultural and economic aspects of breastfeeding are now receiving publicity. In many Third World countries, where until recently breastfeeding was the norm, bottle feeding is becoming more common, apparently in response to Western cultural influences. This has been accompanied by an increase in the incidence of infection, overfeeding, and illness from incorrectly prepared milk. There is also a widespread suspicion that manufacturers' advertising and promotion of artificial feeding have in some cases been motivated more by the idea of profit than by the actual benefits they might bring to mothers and babies. Other special, cultural, and economic factors—such as a woman's need to go back to work after giving birth—obviously have an influence as well.

FEELING PAIN

We still accept the idea that newborn babies do not feel as much pain as they do later, as demonstrated by the continuing practice in the United States of circumcising newborn babies

without anesthetics. If it were necessary to remove an equivalent area of highly sensitive skin from some other part of the body, say the little finger, I think most people would be horrified if it were done without an anesthetic; and yet few demand this for circumcision.

Little systematic research has been done on the baby's perceptions of pain, which is all to the good since no one wants to hurt babies deliberately simply to find out how they react. It does not take psychological research to indicate that babies do feel pain. Direct observation of any baby who has to have a blood test shows us that. Blood samples are commonly obtained by pricking the baby's heel with a small stylette and collecting the drops in a container. The normal reaction of a baby to this procedure is immediately to try and withdraw his foot and to wail with anguish. He may also tense all his muscles and turn a bright red. If we were recording his heartbeat and breathing patterns, we would find that these change rapidly as well. But the reaction varies greatly from baby to baby, depending both on his individual temperament and on his state of alertness at the time. And the reactions of the baby to pain can be modified—for instance, the heartrate increases after circumcision can be reduced by having the baby suck at the same time.

It has been observed that a newborn baby's sleep patterns are disturbed after a heel prick, and this also proves to be so after circumcision. In one study the disturbance followed very soon after circumcision; in a second study there was a prolonged period of wakefulness and fussing, which was then followed by an increase in quiet sleep states. Circumcision has also been put forward as the cause of some of the sex differences that have been noted in studies of newborn babies. Most of these studies have been done in the United States on a population where the majority of males are circumcised at birth. It may be that some differences between male and female babies are due to this procedure rather than to any innate differences.[20]

Babies who have to go into special-care units after birth because they are very small or sick undergo a large number of unpleasant procedures: repeated blood tests, intravenous drips, tubes down their throats to help them breathe. These are obviously unavoidable, but they may affect the way the baby behaves for a time afterward.

TOUCH AND TEMPERATURE

The baby at birth has a large number of reflex responses to being touched at different spots. Most of these are already present when he is in the uterus, and some will disappear soon after birth. The rooting reflex, for instance, occurs when the baby's cheek is touched to one side of the mouth: he turns his head toward the touch. If the baby's palm is touched, he will close his fingers as if to grip. If the back of his foot is touched firmly, he may bend his leg at the knee and hip and then straighten it out again, the so-called placing reflex. If the baby is stroked firmly down the back just to one side of the spine, he will curve his back in to the side being stroked—this has been called the salamander reflex because of its similarity to the back movements of a salamander when it is walking. We do not yet have explanations for many of these touch reflexes. The rooting reflex obviously serves to bring a nipple touching the cheek in direct contact with the mouth so that it can be sucked on—but why the salamander reflex?

Another observation that shows the baby's responsiveness to touch can be made when he is lying in a crib and crying but not hungry. It is often enough simply to place a hand firmly on his chest or tummy to get him to stop. Other more controlled studies were done of babies' behavior when being undressed, as well as the effects of blowing air at them. Girls, for some reason, react much more strongly than boys.

Temperature control in babies is very delicate, and they tend to lose heat rapidly. They do have special reserves of fat under the skin around the shoulders, which can be used to help make extra heat and maintain a steady temperature. Simple observation makes it clear that temperature affects a baby's behavior: warm babies who are not hungry tend to go off to sleep while cold ones cry.

RHYTHMS

I have already mentioned the quieting effect on a baby of playing a recording of a heart beating at about 60-80 beats a minute. A light flashing at the same rhythm will have a similar effect. Another kind of rhythmical stimulation has been studied by Anthony Ambrose and Louis Lipsitt.[21] They designed a spe-

cial crib that could be rocked automatically at varying speeds, and they found, not surprisingly, that the optimal speed was 60 rocks a minute. By studying the various lengths and direction of rock, they showed that the most effective was an up-and-down movement of about three inches which began and ended gradually with a fast phase in the middle, like a pendulum in a vertical plane.

Ambrose and Lipsett also found that babies have another kind of rhythmicity. If they gave a baby ten-second periods of rocks at 60 per minute, followed by periods of 20 seconds with no rocking, then each time the rocking began the baby's heartrate and breathing patterns changed. If the periods of rocking were stopped, each time a period of rocking *should* have begun, the baby's heartrate and breathing still showed changes, as if in anticipation. This continued for several minutes after the periods of rocking had stopped.

These studies reveal two new kinds of appreciation of rhythms. One comes from stimulation of that part of the ear called the vestibular mechanism, which is responsible for balance and by which we can tell which way up we are in space. The other is that of periodicity, whereby a baby is able to anticipate a future rhythmic experience from a past one.

IMITATION

If there is one ability that more than any other demonstrates the sophistication of newborn babies, it is that of imitation. In a series of beautifully controlled studies, Andrew Meltzov, working in both England and the United States, has demonstrated that children of two weeks can stick their tongues out or clench and unclench their hands when they watch someone else do these things. This can only be detected by very close analysis of videotape and film and is not immediately obvious to the eye.

The baby in this sort of imitation has to watch another person sticking out a tongue; he then has to realize that his own tongue is equivalent to the other person's, in spite of the fact that he has never seen his own tongue. Without being able to see what he is doing himself, he must match his movements to the ones he does see. These studies are very recent and are likely to have considerable impact on theories of social development in children.

TRANSCRIPT: MRS. C, AGED 25, FIRST BABY (A BOY)

Father	Mother	Midwife
		Look—more, more, more.
	I can't see.	
	(baby is delivered)	
		Oh my goodness me.
	Oh, ah, ah, ah. Ahahah.	
	Oh. Oh, it's a boy. Ah. Ah. Oh dear. Oh, oh. Oh, no. *(during this period, the baby is lying between mother's legs— mother appears ecstatic)*	
	(father kisses and hugs wife)	
	Ah. He . . . he . . . *(laughs)*. Oh.	
		He's gorgeous.
	Oh, no wonder he was kicking like mad.	
Yes.		
		I think that's calling him 'him'.
	Oh, it's a beautiful boy. Oh poppet.	
(laughs)		

(laughs)

Oh.

Oh (laughs) look at him.

Come on, love, sit up for a
second. You can have him
in a mo. Super girl.

We've been waiting such
a long time.

Look at his size—smashing,
isn't he.

Smashing when they come out,
isn't it? Amazing when they
come out, isn't it?

(baby given to mother)

Oh, oh. Oh. Oh look at his
little mouth.

(laughs)

Oh. Oh.

It's lovely. Look at his little
face. His little nails.
Oh. His little squashed-up
nose like your nose (to father).
He has red hair.

He hasn't got red hair.

(laughs and nods agreement)

Father	Mother	Midwife
		We were wrong you know, weren't we?
(laughs)	It's as red as red.	
	Oh. Oh, oh, oh. Look . . .	
Little baby got big feet— he has got big feet, hasn't he?		
	Oh, ah.	She sounds as if she has run a four-minute mile.
	Oh, his cheeks are coming rosy, love.	
		Just give me another push. Bend that leg up and see if you can push the placenta out. Push. Push down against my hand. Push. Come on, push again. OK—rest for a second.
	Look at his little head. Look at his little mouth.	
(laughs) Look at his hand. I bet it's as tiring for him as it is for you.	He's gone to sleep. I wonder whether he was sucking his	

thumb inside. He knows his face, look (*baby touching his face with a hand*). Oh get off (*baby appears to swipe away father's touching fingers*).

Amazing sight.

Ah, I can't believe it.

He can't be ten pounds.

You said eight pounds. I said nine pounds.

Look at his hair. Oh look, it's all fair there.

It's red, isn't it. It's fair round the side too.

It's very difficult to tell. It's red round the top there.

He is going a nice colour now, aren't you (*to baby*)? He's sucking his thumb. How any man can feel sick at it, I don't know (*referring to men feeling sick when present at birth*).

I think the thought is, yes.

Isn't it ghastly?

Oh you poppet. It wasn't bad.

You were terrific, especially when we had some delays. You did

Father	Mother	Midwife
		awfully well. (*to baby*) Stupid child, I don't know what you were getting up to inside— having a whale of a time.
	He was, wasn't he?	
		He came out the right way round. He had turned right round the proper way.
	Oh dear, what did you do that for (*to indistinguishable action by baby*)? He's blowing bubbles. His little hands are all wrinkled—looks like he's done the washing up, doesn't he?	
		So doesn't he look nice?
Yes (*laughs*). Oh dear!		
Oh dear!	He looks . . .	
		It was a girl you were so sure about?
Yes. Every day we had a different idea. That was the trouble.	No. We knew it was going to be a boy, didn't we (*to husband*)?	

That's why it's a boy. Open your eyes then (*to the baby*). Ahh (*laughs*). Can you open your eyes then? He's scratched himself by the look of it, on his face.

No, that's just blood that he brought with him. Give a little push down, love. Give a good push right down into my hand.

Oh (*pain with contraction of third stage of labour*).

Baby is straining away too.

You're not squeezing him too hard, are you?

No, he's resting on me.

Can you do one more? Come on— here it comes.

Oh, he's opened his eyes. there—look, look.

Hello (*as baby opens his eyes for the first time*)!

Don't distract her. She's meant to be pushing.

Sorry.

Oh, he's going (*imitates baby blinking*). Hello (*laughs*).

Father	Mother	Midwife
	Oh, his eyes are all stuck. Hello.	
(laughs) What colour are they?		
	Dark blue.	
Oh yeah!		
	Hello, look. He's got your eyes (to husband). Look, you've got beautiful blue eyes (to baby). What are you looking at me like that for (to baby)?	
		Come on, here it comes (hoping for delivery of placenta).
	Hello. Oh, he's got a beautiful face. Yah (delivery of placenta). How long do they usually take to open their eyes?	
(laughs) Yes, but they're blind, you know.		
		Oh, it varies. Has he opened them now?
	He's got one open now.	
		Another injection coming now. It's a stingy one.
	We will have to give you a	

bath in a minute, won't we (*to baby*). Hello. Hello.

(*laughs*) Well I'm blowed.

Oh no (*at something unseen*). You can really grip, can't you (*to baby*)? Ah (*injection*). A horrible stingy one.

Look at this baby—there (*baby gripping father's finger*).

I told you, didn't I?

Did he seem to hold your finger?

Yes, he did. Missed it before. (*laughs*) Oh dear.

Did he?

He wants to open his mouth—look. We will see if we can give him a feed in a minute.

Would you like to give him to his father?

(*mother gives baby to father*)

Oh, he doesn't like being held by me. Look—he's pulling horrible faces.

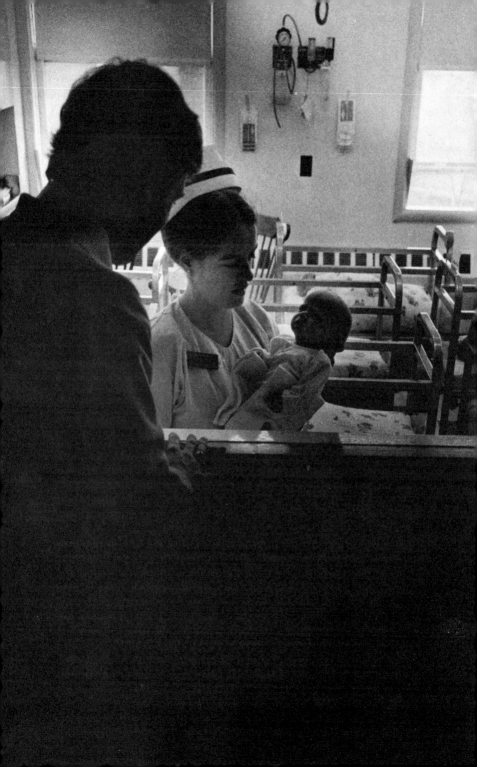

7 / Mother and Child: Separation

One puzzling question about the mother's and baby's behavior after birth is whether there really is the special and unique relationship between them that is known as attachment or bonding. The idea that such a relationship might exist and can be studied arose from animal-behavior work and from the studies of the English psychiatrist John Bowlby of the effects on institutionalized children of physical separation from their parents.

Over the last few years, psychological approaches to this question have developed in several ways. One is to inquire into the much broader area of the baby's social relationships with the world in general, and I will discuss this in the next chapter. Another is to look into the effects of separation in greater detail: Does separating mother and baby after birth interfere with early relationships in such a way as to affect their behavior when they are reunited?

The most common form of separation following birth occurs when a baby has to go into a special-care unit away from his mother. If such a separation does seem to have an adverse effect, then obviously it should be as brief as it can be made, and only where absolutely necessary. Mothers and fathers should also be encouraged to see and handle their babies whenever possible while they are in special care.

Childbirth in humans, at least until a hundred years ago, often resulted in the death of either the child or the mother. During this period, in terms of the continuing survival of the human race as a whole, it would not have made sense if the mother and baby had formed an immediate and lasting tie at birth. If the mother died, then the baby would have to be able to accept some other

caregiver without too much upset in his life. If the baby died, the mother would have to be able to mourn but then go on and have more children. So one would expect any special relationship between the two to develop over a period of time. This is in contrast to some species of birds where the newborn chick very rapidly learns the features of people, animals, other birds, or objects to which it is exposed, and afterward shows special behavior toward them. If in humans the relationship does develop slowly, initial separation might have only minor effects which could be compensated for later if all went well.

When babies have to go into special-care units, it is difficult to know whether effects on the behavior of mother or baby come from the separation itself or from the reasons the baby had to go into the unit (prematurity, sickness, and so on). It is therefore more useful, perhaps, to look at evidence from separations involving normal full-term babies. A great deal of the work done on very early separation has been carried out by Marshall Klaus and John Kennell.[1] In one of their studies, done in Guatemala, a group of nine mothers were given their naked babies immediately after they had left the delivery room. A second group of nine mothers and babies were separated according to the usual hospital routine. The babies in both groups were then sent to the newborn nursery for the next twelve hours and returned to their mothers for their first feeding. Observations during this feeding of the amount of maternal fondling, kissing, gazing into the baby's face, and holding him close showed that such behavior was greater among those mothers who had had early contact with their infants.

In the context of the importance of early mother-infant contact, Klaus and Kennell quote two other observations. The first is the case of an accident at an Israeli hospital, where two mothers were given each other's babies by mistake. This was only discovered two weeks later, and when efforts were made to return the babies to their proper families, it was found that each mother had become so attached to the baby she had that she did not want to change. It was the fathers who for family reasons wanted the error corrected. Second, they cite a study done in the United States with two groups of mothers who had expressed a desire to breastfeed. One group was given their babies to suckle shortly after birth, and the other did not have contact with theirs

till some sixteen hours later. No mother in either group had to stop breastfeeding for physical reasons. But two months later, the mothers who had had their infants to suckle right after birth were still all breastfeeding, while of the others five out of six had stopped.

Perhaps even more interesting than these observations was a study Klaus and Kennell did themselves.[2] They studied twenty-eight mothers of normal full-term babies. Half of the group was given the traditional American contact with their babies: a glimpse of the baby shortly after birth, brief contact and identification at six to twelve hours, and then visits for twenty to thirty minutes every four hours for bottle feeds. The other fourteen mothers were given their naked babies for one hour within the first three hours and also five extra hours' contact on each afternoon for three days after delivery. These mothers therefore had a total of an extra sixteen hours' contact with their babies.

At one month the mothers and babies returned to the hospital for three separate observations: an interview, a period of observation of each mother as her baby was being examined by a pediatrician, and a period of observation as the mother fed her baby. The mothers who had had the extra sixteen hours of extended contact showed a greater tendency to pick their babies up when they cried, though the babies were not hungry and had just had their diapers changed. These extended-contact mothers also stood closer to the baby as he was being examined and were more likely to soothe him if he became upset during the course of the examination. In the observations of feeding, these mothers spent significantly more time fondling their babies and holding them *en face*. At another examination after one year, the extended-contact mothers spent more time helping the doctor and soothing the child if he cried.[3] At two years, five mothers were randomly selected from each group to see how they talked to their children. The extended-contact mothers used twice as many questions, fewer words per proposition, more adjectives, and fewer commands. It therefore appears from all this that sixteen hours of extra contact at birth had an effect lasting for at least two years.

Most of the mothers in this case had little education, came from extremely poor social circumstances, and were having illegitimate children. I think that these factors may have had an

influence on the prolongation of the affects. Very large longitudinal studies carried out over many years all indicate that the parents' social class is the best single indicator of what a child's physical and mental development will be by the age of twelve. In the poor social circumstances of the mothers in this study, the extra time and attention that one group received may have been enough to make a difference that continued. If the mothers had come from a middle-class background, I believe the differences found would have been compensated for by the relatively good environment the middle classes usually enjoy. There are two other studies that I think support this idea, done by Andrew Whiten in England and by Herbert Leiderman and Marjorie Seashore in the United States.[4] Both were mainly of middle-class mothers and examined the effects of separation when babies go into special care. Because of this, again we have to remember that differences in behavior of mother or baby might be due either to the separation or to the reason for the separation.

Whiten looked at one group of ten mothers and babies who had been separated after birth. The babies had gone into special care for between two and fourteen days for a variety of minor medical ailments, such as mild jaundice; they were considered to be medically normal on discharge from the unit. For comparison he took eleven other mothers and babies who had not been separated, and at intervals over the first year observed the mothers and babies from both groups in their homes.

At three weeks he asked the mothers to keep diaries with details of their baby's behavior for twenty-four hours. Dividing the day into five-minute blocks, the mothers recorded the amount of time the baby was in or out of his crib, and the time he spent crying, fussing, being held, being fed, being asleep, drowsy, or awake. Whiten found that the mothers in the separated group recorded over twice as much crying from their babies as the mothers of the nonseparated group. More detailed examination of the diaries indicated that the separated babies not only cried more frequently but also cried longer each time. The separated and nonseparated mothers intervened to stop their babies from crying, by picking them up and such, an equal amount of time over the twenty-four hours, but because the separated babies cried more frequently, their mothers intervened proportionately less.

When Whiten observed the mothers and babies at one month and two months, there were significant differences between the two groups in the amount of time mothers and babies spent looking and smiling at one another. The separated group looked and smiled less, and indeed the social smile appeared later in these babies. It could be that social behavior gradually increases the more mother and baby are in contact, and that it takes the separated mothers and babies time to catch up. The same would apply to the baby's ability to distinguish his own mother from a stranger on the basis of sight, hearing, and smell. It looks as though these abilities are learned by having experience of the mother, and if this is missing initially, then the learning will be delayed by the length of time the mother and baby are separated.

Interestingly, when Whiten observed his subjects at three and four months he found that most of the differences between the two groups had disappeared. There are two possible explanations: first, that Whiten's mothers were middle-class and the effects of their environment had made up for any differences caused by the original separation. The alternative is that, as the baby becomes able to do more complex things and to interact in more complex ways with his mother and the environment, so the effects of separation become "diluted" or find expression in other behavior. Although the later observations in Whiten's study have not yet been fully analyzed, there is evidence that there may be some truth in the latter explanation.

Leiderman and Seashore studied three groups of mothers. One group delivered premature infants who had to be admitted to the special-care unit for three weeks or more. During this time they were allowed to view their babies from the nursery window but never had a chance to touch them. A second group had premature infants who were admitted to the special-care unit, but the mothers were allowed in to touch and handle their babies in the incubators and cribs. The third group of mothers had full-term normal babies who were not separated. All mothers and babies were followed up for two years or more, and the researchers made observations of the kinds of behavior they judged to show maternal attachment: behavior involving close bodily contact between mother and baby; behavior involving more distant contact (looking, smiling); and time devoted solely to interacting with the baby but excluding direct caregiving procedures (feed-

ing, changing). The mother's self-confidence was also assessed by means of a questionnaire.

The results showed that separation seemed to have very little effect on the time the mothers spent with their babies after discharge from the hospital. Nor did it affect the time they devoted to interacting with the babies outside the usual caregiving routines. There were, however, significant differences between those mothers who had been separated and those who had not in the amount of caressing they did and in the amount of time they held their babies close. The separated mothers scored lower, and also spent less time smiling at their babies. There were at first only minor differences between the behavior of mothers who had been allowed contact with their babies in the special-care unit and those who had no contact at all, although at one year the mothers allowed contact were touching their babies more. The questionnaires given to rate the mother's feelings showed that separation lowered self-confidence only in those mothers who were having their first baby, and even for these only at first. Assessments at one month and twelve months revealed no difference in maternal self-confidence in the three groups.

Follow-up one year from leaving the hospital showed that the effects of separation on the mothers' attitude and behavior had almost disappeared. Differences in the way the mothers behaved with their children seemed to be determined more by the baby's position in the family in relation to brothers and sisters, by the sex of the baby, and by the family's social class. At a year the mothers of first-born male infants were touching them more and giving them more attention than those mothers who had later-born or female infants.

When the children were followed up at twenty-one months, a rather different and surprising finding was made. Of twenty-two families where the mothers had premature children and no contact with them, five had got divorced; in the families with premature children who had contact, one had got divorced; in the group of mothers with no separation, there had been no divorces. Leiderman and Seashore suggest that the newborn period does have an effect, albeit nonspecific, by acting as a stress that might create trouble within the family structure. But there is a possibility that the stresses in family relationships may have been present before the baby was even born and that these stresses

had contributed to the child's prematurity. Support for this idea also comes from one study done of children who had in some way been injured by their parents.[5] By comparing the group of children who had this misfortune with their brothers or sisters, it was shown that the abused children had had a higher than normal incidence of admission to special-care baby units, but their mothers had also had a significantly greater incidence of complications during the pregnancy with the abused children than with their brothers and sisters. Other work, by D. H. Stott, seems to show that stress in family relationships before a child is born may influence the chances of trouble with the baby after delivery, but the studies were done retrospectively and it is probable that the trouble with the child after birth was related to continuing upset in the parents' relationship.[6]

Leiderman's studies on separation were done with middle-class mothers, and the differences between his findings and those of Klaus and Kennell may be explained by the compensatory effects offered by a better environment. Still, the work of Klaus and Kennell suggests that, in very adverse social circumstances, a little help at an early stage may make a substantial difference in later maternal behavior.

Today, with modern pediatric care, babies who are born very small have an excellent chance of growing up into normal healthy adults. But to their mothers and fathers they must appear to be especially vulnerable at birth, and parents frequently voice their concern as wonder that such a small baby can ever grow to be normal in size. One recent report found little difference during follow-up between the mothers of premature babies and those of normal full-term babies, but the mothers of the premature baby still perceived him as being the "weak little one."

Investigators at University College Hospital in London followed up one hundred and sixty babies who weighed less than 1500 grams (3.25 pounds) at birth and therefore spent some time in special care.[7] At this hospital, every attempt was made to minimize the separation. Parents were allowed in to see, touch, hold, and care for their babies as much as conditions permitted; even brothers and sisters were allowed to visit. After discharge, most parents were found to go through the same stages. First there was the "honeymoon stage," lasting from one to three weeks, when the parents were excited and sometimes almost

euphoric about the baby, whose continued existence had seemed so tenuous earlier. This phase was frequently followed by one of exhaustion, when the euphoria waned and the mothers began to complain of minor problems in managing the baby and especially in feeding. This stage might last a few days or even weeks, and sometimes ended when the baby started to smile and generally became more responsive. In the next phase the problems rapidly disappeared; the mother looked better and handled her baby with more confidence and increasing pleasure.

The researchers also found that getting fathers to come in and handle their babies in the unit had an effect similar to that found in the Swedish study mentioned in Chapter Five. Most fathers became frequent visitors to the unit and many regularly attended follow-up clinics after the babies' discharge; a few even brought the baby in without the mother. They asked many questions and were obviously involved in their child's day-to-day care. The investigators speculated as to whether in fact very low birth weight might be actually advantageous to the formation of paternal relationships, since several weeks of visiting the child in the hospital might allow the father time gradually to accept both the child and the inevitable changes in his relationship with his wife. Leiderman also notes the importance of bringing families, rather than just mothers, into the special units—he feels that the stresses of excluding one parent could have a very severe effect on family relationships, which many would say are stretched enough even after the birth of a full-term child in ideal circumstances.

Some hospitals have instituted a "nesting period," when mothers of premature babies can come back to hospital and take complete care of their babies for two or three days before going home. In one such hospital, many of the wives insisted that the facilities should be extended to husbands as well. Finally, it is worth noting that parents of premature babies, when asked what kind of help they needed and wanted, were given a choice of doctors, social workers, psychologists, family, and friends. But their first choice was other parents who had themselves been separated from their children. They were also very definite that they wanted the help to be within their home area so that they did not have to travel miles to get it.

In summary, then: for a nonspecific time after birth, there does seem to be a period in the developing relationship between mothers, fathers, and babies when separation may be detrimental. But the relationships will also be influenced by the condition of the baby, whether he is small or sick. Stresses and strains will continue for some time after the end of the separation, but on the whole and given a reasonable environment (the actual definition of this is exceedingly difficult to make, though one supposes from the studies that some middle-class families provide a bit of it), the effects will gradually disappear or become diluted. This would of course lead us to stress the importance not only of ensuring that the child gets the benefits of medical aid while in hospital but also of at least being aware of the influences of his social environment when he gets home. It is possible that an improvement of social circumstances might be of more benefit to health than all the medicine we have available.

TRANSCRIPT: MRS. D, AGED 27, FIRST BABY (A GIRL)

Father	Mother	Midwife
It's a boy!		It's a girl!
	It's a girl! Oh, it's not, is it?	
Very nice, I got my things sorted out wrong.		
	Oh.	Beautiful, absolutely lovely.
	Oh.	
She's a beaut, Jo. (kisses wife)		Here we are Jo, alright? You can have her in just a minute.
	Oh, oh. Where is it?	
Congratulations.		
	What are we going to call it?	
(laughs) Bruce. We'll think of something. Well, I'd better . . .		Jo, can you put your feet down, love? If you want to, just

Take it easy—that's it.

    relax. It's a bit puddly, but don't worry about that.

    I wanted a boy.

Well, we've got plenty of things, haven't we? I thought we had everything.

    It can't play rugby. Everyone said it was going to be a boy. What are we going to put her in?

    She's a nice size, yes.

    She's a big one too.

    God, that was a quickie, wasn't it? What time was I?

    Forty-six minutes.

    What's that?

Yeah—no, I wasn't disappointed.

    No, it wasn't a boy. I know what Ma will do—bitch.

No. Oh dear, oh dear.

    She would even choose our boy's name.

So what? She might have wanted a little girl.

Father	Mother	Midwife
		Here you are, Jo.
	(baby given to mother)	
	Ah, oh (greets baby). What a funny face (to baby).	
Oh, she's got your nose. Now then.		
	What a funny creature you are.	
Right. Well, I'm going to phone.		
	No, wait (to father). Oh (pain). Just for a minute.	
OK.		
	She's just like a little bird, isn't she? Can you take that silly hat off (referring to hospital cap worn by father)?	
In a minute when I leave here.		
	No, not to my knowledge anyway (whispers to baby). What do you want (to baby)? Come on (to baby).	
		Do you want to spend a penny, Jo?
(blows kisses to baby)		

Yes. Is that everything?

Funny! Yah (*as placenta is delivered*). It's slimy.

It's only the soft tissue afterbirth.

What?

You look like Sue (*to father*). It's a little girl.

Yes, it's a little girl.

It's a little girl.

Oh, you're joking.

Oh, but we won't tell them that.

Everyone was so sure it would be a boy. I said that I could see you better with a girl.

So much for my work . . .

Just as well I can't see down there, I hate the sight of blood. Whoo, whoo (*to the baby*).

(*sighs*) Not in the slightest.

Are you sure?

Of course I'm sure.

This is a little bit sore, Jo. I just want to check. Jolly good, great super. Just one little episiotomy to suture.

Father	Mother	Midwife
		You should be fairly numb—that's what this injection's for. We can give you a bit more. You did incredibly well. Really great.
That's it? Well, well, mere details now, mere details.		
Listen, I think I'll go and phone. All right?	Don't go, please.	
What? No, I'm on the . . .	We haven't decided on a name yet, you silly ass.	
George, George.	What are we going to have?	
No, it doesn't matter, doesn't matter at the moment. We'll just say it's a girl.		
	How much does she weigh?	
	Wait and find out.	Don't know yet—we'll weigh her in a minute.
Ah, eight pounds and three ounces.		

She's round the eight mark.
I'll tell you in a minute
when I've weighed her.

She's not as big as everyone
said she would be.

(baby taken away from mother)

Eight pounds.

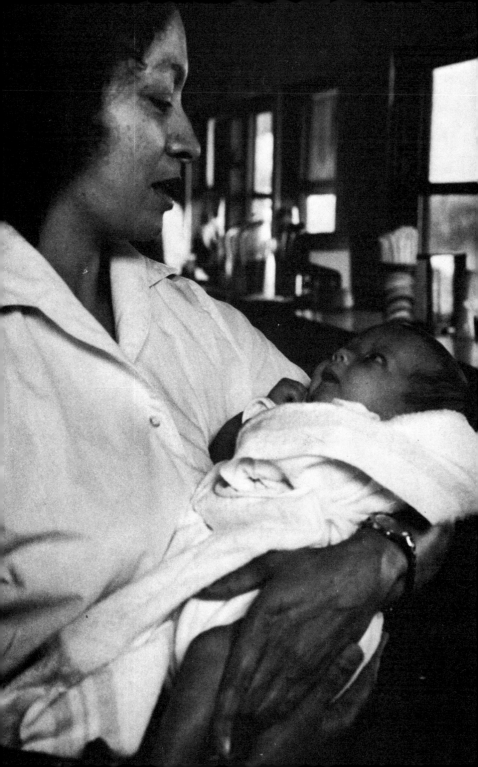

8 / Mother and Child: Socialization

At birth and during the first few days afterward, babies show a very large range of spontaneous behavior. This includes sucking and mouthing, sleeping, peeing, trying to get their hand into their mouths, smiling, erections in the male (I don't know whether anyone has looked at the female equivalent), hiccoughing, burping, defecating, moving their arms and legs, crying. There are also forms of behavior which are more directly responses to changes in the environment, such as following faces with the eyes, turning the head toward a sound, withdrawing the leg when the heel is pricked, startling at loud noises, quieting down when held.

Observations of these kinds of behavior in newborns have been made by many different investigators, and the general conclusion has been that each baby is moderately consistent in the behavior he shows over the first days of life—but that there is a great variation between individual babies in the amount of each kind they show. Thus Baby Jane, if she is good at following peoples' faces with her eyes on the third day after birth, is likely to be good at this on day ten, but over this period she might be consistently inaccurate in getting her hand into her mouth. Baby David may not look at faces over this period but be consistently able to suck on his fingers. No one yet knows exactly what factors are responsible for this variation between babies.

But variation or no, it has been suggested that there are certain features that are universally attractive to mothers in the period immediately after birth. These might include the baby's helplessness, his cry, or his physical appearance. Irenaus Eibl-Eibesfeldt had emphasized some of the unique qualities of the human baby:

115

the large forehead, small face, large eyes, chubby cheeks, small mouth, and unequal proportions (the baby's head is large at birth compared to his body).[1]

An experiment to see what constituted "babyish" proportions was done by B. Garner and L. Wallach using silhouettes of adult heads, baby heads, and "super-baby" heads with accentuated foreheads and smaller chins than normal.[2] These were shown to a series of American college students who, asked to pick out the one they thought most babyish, showed a consistent tendency to choose the super-baby silhouettes; this tendency was stronger among the women students than among the men. Eibl-Eibesfeldt has also done studies in different cultures in an attempt to show that the pattern of a baby's smile is the same in all children, and also that it is interpreted the same way in all cultures.[3] It does seem from his evidence that the pattern of the smile is universal, but it seems likely that the interpretation of its meaning must be different, not only in different cultures but according to the individual circumstances at particular moments.

Not all mothers like certain characteristics of a baby at birth. Some films of mothers with their babies in the delivery room immediately after birth show them turning away from the baby in disgust, with such remarks as "Oh no" or "Oh God, it looks just like its father." Howard Moss and K. S. Robson found in one of their studies that most of the women described feelings of strangeness and unfamiliarity toward their babies which persisted for at least the first few weeks of life.[4] Asked when she first felt love, when she ceased feeling strange with her child, and when the baby first became a person to her, a mother's answer frequently involved the baby's "looking" as if he were recognizing objects in his surroundings.

In one of my studies I asked ninety-seven mothers who had delivered their first babies two months previously when they first felt love for their infants. For forty it was during pregnancy, for twenty-three it was at birth, for twenty-six it was during the first week, and for eight it was some time after the end of the first week. I also asked the same mothers whether they thought that their love became stronger at any particular stage and, if so, when. Thirty thought their love grew greater at birth, twenty-nine during the first two weeks, and ten during the second two weeks. Twenty-eight thought that their love did not grow

greater. There is great variation here, and it suggests that for many women the development of maternal love is a fairly gradual affair.

I have proposed earlier that one reason for a gradually developing relationship between mother and baby is that there used to be a very high deathrate at birth. Another partial explanation might be that affection between two people has to be based on learning specific characteristics of the other person. Initially one's response may be a reaction to some general feature of another but, as time goes on, the reaction may only occur when the feature is singled out as belonging individually to that one person.

Our knowledge of the mother's part in the developing relationship is taken a step further by John Newson, in a paper with the deliberately ambiguous title "Towards a Theory of Infant Understanding."[5] He proposes that "the human infant is pre-programmed to emit 'signals' and that these signals are of such a kind that his mother will inevitably pay attention to them. She is equally bound to endow them with social significance." This comes back to the observations I made of mothers with their babies in the delivery room immediately after birth; I found that in some cases the mother was even then putting social connotations on the baby's actions—something also found by H. S. Bennett in the United States, when he made a detailed study of the course of development in three infants during the first weeks of life.[6] He proposes from his observations that the caregivers (and in this case they were nurses, since the babies were going to be fostered out) use the facial expressions and spontaneous behavior of a baby to construct a fantasy about his personality, and then use this fantasy personality as the basis for handling the infant. For instance, one baby who stopped crying whenever he was picked up was seen by the nurse as "socially responsive," and another baby showing similar behavior was regarded by his nurse as "exploitative and spoilt." The first baby received maximal individual attention, and the second was left to cry.

In the words of Newson, "Human babies become human beings because they are treated as if they were human beings."[7] It would perhaps be possible to take that statement a step further: "Human babies become the type of human being they grow up to be only because they were treated like that kind of human be-

ing." At birth and even before, however, a baby has developed in such a way as to create the basis for social existence. He responds more to human beings than to objects, is more likely to turn his head toward a human voice than to a bell, and is more likely to look at a human face than at a flashing light. So just as the biology and biochemistry of the baby have developed by birth so that he is capable of breathing the oxygen from the atmosphere that surrounds him, so he has also developed in biological and biochemical ways that will allow him to live in a world of social relationships. This social milieu is one that the human organism has adapted to over millions of years, just as much as it has to the atmosphere. However, unlike the specific oxygen content of the air, social relationships are extremely variable.

The development of socialization in the first two weeks or so can take on the form of preferential behavior toward the mother as opposed to strangers. What processes of learning are involved, and how do they work?

First I would like to indicate how they do not work. It was proposed by Konrad Lorenz that the term "imprinting" should be used to apply to the special kind of learning found in many species of birds shortly after hatching. These newborn birds could respond socially to a surprising range of objects and would attempt to nestle against animals, moving boxes, flashing lights, or anything else that happened to be present at the moment after hatching. As a result of imprinting on an object, the young birds came to prefer it to other objects and eventually would come to direct their social behavior exclusively toward the familiar object. Work done by Patrick Bateson with chicks has led him to some further conclusions about the learning processes that occur in imprinting.[8] He confirmed that the development of a preference for a familiar object began in the chick at a very early stage in life, but that it lasted only until the bird became more familiar with its environment. Before the learning began, the chicks would work actively to present themselves with an object from which they could learn, and during learning they would work to present themselves with different views of the object to which they were becoming attached. Bateson also found that the preference for one object over another lasted longer or shorter according to how long the chicks were exposed to the object initially.

The term "imprinting" has been loosely used to cover many different types of behavior in many different species, but in the way that it was used originally the phenomenon has not been shown to occur in humans. This is perhaps just as well, for if human infants did show a form of imprinting, by which they begin to display specific behavior toward the first object or person they have experience of immediately after birth, it is likely that this behavior would be directed to the masked faces of the medical attendants, with unfortunate implications for later development.

Although human babies do show different behavior toward their own mothers as against strangers, this does not appear to occur immediately after birth, and in any case is only a very small variation in the baby's total repertoire of behavior. This is indicated in a study done by Louis Sander and his colleagues, who arranged for a group of babies to be looked after by one nurse in a rooming-in situation for the first ten days of life (all these babies were eventually going to be fostered).[9] The babies were fed on a self-demand feeding schedule from the first twenty-four hours. At ten days, an unfamiliar though highly experienced nurse took over the care of each child, again in the rooming-in situation. This resulted in specific disturbances in each baby's behavior, especially in the patterning of his periods of activity and sleep and crying, showing by small changes in the amount and timing of certain actions that he knew his caregiver was different.

Bateson did feel, from his work with chicks, that there were two issues relevant to humans. First, certain stages of development are crucial for the acquisition of preferences and habits. Second, the young are far from being passive little creatures but play an active part in determining the kind of stimulation they get. The first of these issues has obvious implications for mother-child separation. It seems possible that there is a sensitive period in humans immediately after birth for the development of relations between mother and child, and that this could get upset by separation, at least in the short term. The second issue is more complicated. As a newborn child does seem to show preferential responses toward people rather than objects, he is to a degree playing an active part in the type of stimulation he is getting. However, a chick is born feathered and mobile, and this mobility gives it the chance of seeking out its stimulation. The human

newborn can only attempt to call the stimulation to himself by crying, and then try and hold it there.

But how much do the infant and the mother influence one another's behavior? David Levy, in a series of observations of mother-newborn relationships, looked at mothers' greeting response when their babies were brought in by a nurse the first two or three times after birth.[10] He found that there was great variation in these greetings and that a mother who greeted her baby on one occasion might not do so on another. Mothers rated as very maternal seemed no different in this respect from those rated as not very maternal at all. It seemed that the greeting depended mainly on the baby's behavior. On those occasions when he was quiet and awake, the mother always greeted him, but when he was crying she greeted him only about once in three times and when he was asleep only once in six. Levy felt that it was possible to infer devotion, interest, affection, tenderness, and that it was possible just to conjecture that there was an underlying feeling of possession, as of having something highly treasured. It is also possible to infer from the study that the mother's behavior is very much dependent on that of her baby, and that simple observations of a mother's behavior could be grossly misleading about her actual feelings. Levy also found that to some extent the mothers' behavior was a result of how they expected a situation to develop. Thus he found that the mother's anticipation of the problems of feeding served to curtail her greeting.

Work by Louis Sander also indicates how baby and mother each start off acting fairly autonomously, without at first synchronizing their behavior, and only gradually over the weeks adapt to one another's routines.[11] He had three groups of nine babies in three different situations. Group 1 spent the first ten days in a nursery and then were roomed-in with one of two nurses, X or Y, for eighteen days before being fostered out. Group 2 was roomed-in with a nurse for ten days, changed to another nurse for eighteen days, and then fostered out (this group I have already mentioned). Finally, babies in Group 3 were roomed-in with their mothers for five days, and then went home with the mothers and were with them thereafter.

Many fascinating findings emerge from this study. For in-

stance, when the babies in Group 1, who had been in the nursery, were given to the nurses on day ten, those with Nurse Y began to cry less, while those given to Nurse X continued as before. When Sander looked at the behavior of the nurses to discover what might be responsible for the difference, he found that Nurse X followed very simple, nowadays generally held precepts of infant care, including demand feeding. She had the feeling that all that was required was to love the babies. Although she perceived individual differences between the infants in her care, she did not often draw on this information to vary her method of dealing with them. Nurse Y, on the other hand, was always using her keen ability to perceive individual differences and trying out different ways of caregiving which these differences might specifically require from her. "In other words her aim was in the direction of establishing unique interactions upon which stability in an individual infant's course would become predictable for her."

The Sander study also revealed much else of interest. From the activity records of individual babies it appears that some children in the first few days of life show recurrent peaks of activity every three to five hours within a twenty-four-hour span. These periods of activity at first hardly coincide at all with the periods of caregiving activity. But by the fifteenth day the times of peak activity have lost their periodicity, while sleep periods have grown longer and tend to gather at night. At the same time, the baby's periods of activity and the caregiving activity have become more synchronized, suggesting that in the ten to fifteen days following birth the baby and his caregiver are beginning to get themselves coordinated.

Theodore Gaensbauer set out to discover whether the distribution of awake, alert periods relative to feeds was different for demand-fed babies than for schedule-fed ones.[12] He found that the total amount of wakefulness in the two groups was very much the same, which suggested that "there may be intrinsic mechanisms which regulate the proportionate amounts of time an infant will spend in sleep and wakefulness." However, the distribution of the periods of alertness was indeed different. Demand-fed infants showed little wakefulness during the feeding and for most of the time between feeds, except for a period of

high alertness just before each feed began. The schedule-fed babies had their wakefulness spread less unevenly, since almost all of it occurred just before or after feeds. It is worth noting in passing that the demand-fed group appeared to have an intrinsic sleep-wake cycle, which ran over approximately four hours.

A large number of recent studies have looked at the behavior of mothers and babies together in detail. Some of this work was pioneered by Martin Richards, and his examination, frame by frame, of films taken of mothers and babies smiling at one another shows a very precise sequencing of behavior between the two partners.[13] For instance, a mother would smile at her baby, and the baby would watch with close attention; when she stopped smiling, the baby's activity would increase and at the moment of maximum "pumped-upness" he would smile; if during this period the mother did not stop all her own activity to let the baby do his smile, he would get upset and fretful.

With Judy Bernal, Richards has more recently been doing detailed observations of babies in the period around birth to see how a mother's behavior influences her baby's and vice-versa.[14] They found that one particular aspect of feeding was different: among bottle-feeding mothers it was usually the mother who pulled the nipple from the baby's mouth; among breastfeeders, the feeds were ended just as often by the baby's releasing the nipple. Richards and Bernal also found that kissing, rocking, and affectionate touching were more common with breastfeeders, while rubbing, patting, jiggling, and concern about bringing up gas predominated among bottle-feeders.

When observing infants and mothers together it is frequently difficult to tell who starts a sequence and who ends it. For instance, on one of Andrew Whiten's videotapes of a feed, a mother who was holding her child to the breast with one hand under his neck suddenly reached for a cloth. About five seconds later, the child vomited and the mother had the cloth ready by his mouth. Looking at the videotape there was no way to tell how she had known in advance that the baby was going to vomit. When we played the tape back to this mother, she explained that she had felt the muscles tighten in the back of his neck, and she knew from previous experience what that forecast.

This kind of detail on the interactive behavior of mother and child can give us clues as to how a fetus actually does develop into a social being. Perhaps psychologists are attempting to be modern-day prophets, taking over from the astrologers of yesterday.

Epilogue

If I have any one strong belief after reviewing the research and my own experiences, it is that childbirth is, in the main, a normal physiological process that might be enhanced if women felt, and were encouraged to feel, competent at it and confident in themselves and their bodies.

It seems a pity that in our society success and social status are so often associated with the immediate acquirement of money. With this, the position of women in childbearing and childrearing, which now (although not always in the past) brings little financial reward, has been relegated to a secondary position. The French, ever realistic, give benefits to parents of between $1200 and $1800 if they attend an antenatal clinic and bring the child for regular checkups over the first year of his life. Where concern for the child's actual health may not motivate them to come to the clinics, financial reward does. (This was also a far-sighted investment in economic terms, for high attendance at the clinics has reduced the incidence of death and handicap, and the government has to spend less on the provision of special homes and facilities.)

I also think it necessary to remember that the system of reproduction developed as a whole, as part of a larger biological system. Its features did not evolve independently. It is not just that mothers developed to be specially good at looking after babies or babies to be specially attractive to their mothers. They are both part of a system designed to make sure that children will grow into adults, and reproduce in turn, thus enabling the species to continue. It is not just the child's relationship with his

mother that matters, but his relationships with his mother, father, other human beings, and the environment in general.

Finally I am aware that the book covers only a few facets of the relationship between an infant and his environment before, during, and after birth and between a mother and her baby. It could hardly deal with all the interdependent behavior and feelings that occur twenty-four hours a day and seven days a week. Nor can it give any idea of how stressful and demanding this involvement is. At best I have sketched in one or two marks on a huge, intricate, and varied canvas, knowing that the whole will always be far more than the constituent parts and that the picture can never be finished.

References
Suggested Reading
Index

References

1 Life Before Birth

1. L. Watson, *Supernature* (London: Hodden and Stoughton, 1973).
2. L. W. Sontag and R. F. Wallce, "The Effect of Cigarette Smoking During Pregnancy upon Fetal Heart Rate," *American Journal of Obstetrics and Gynecology*, 1935, *29*, 77-82. L. W. Sontag and R. F. Wallace, "The Movement Response of the Human Fetus to Sound Stimuli," *Child Development*, 1935, *6*, 253-258.
3. F. E. Hytten, "Metabolic Adaptation of Pregnancy in the Prevention of Handicap Through Antenatal Care." In A. C. Turnbull and F. P. Woodford, eds., *Review of Research Practice*, *18* (Amsterdam: Elsevier, 1976).
4. L. W. Sontag, "Changes in the Rate of the Human Fetal Heartbeat in Response to Vibratory Stimuli," *American Journal of the Diseases of Childhood*, 1936, *51*, 583-589.
5. J. C. Grimwade et al., "Human Fetal Heartrate Change and Movement in Response to Sound and Vibration," *American Journal of Obstetrics and Gynecology*, 1971, *109*, 86-90.
6. D. Walker et al., "Intrauterine Noise, a Component of the Fetal Environment," *American Journal of Obstetrics and Gynecology*, 1971, *109*, 91-95.
7. L. Salk, "The Role of the Heartbeat in the Relationship Between Mother and Infant," *Scientific American*, March 1973.
8. L. W. Sontag, "Implications of Fetal Behavior and Environment for Adult Personalities," *Annals of the New York Academy of Science*, 1966, *134*(2), 782.

2 Social and Psychological Factors

1. Office of Population Censuses and Surveys, *Classification of Occupations* (London: HMSO, 1976).
2. E. C. Mann, "The Role of Emotional Determinants in Habitual Abortion," *Surgical Clinics of North America*, 1959, *37*, 447.
3. S. Rosen, "Emotional Factors in Nausea and Vomiting of Pregnancy," *Psychiatric Quarterly*, 1955, *29*, 621.
4. A. Blau et al., "The Psychogenic Etiology of Premature Births," *Psychosomatic Medicine*, 1963, *25*, 201.
5. A. Coppen, "Psychosomatic Aspects of Pre-Eclamptic Toxemia,"

Journal of Psychosomatic Research, 1958, *2*, 241-265.
6. H. Bakow et al., "The Relation Between Newborn Behaviour and Mother-Child Interaction" (Paper presented at Society for Research in Child Development, March 1973).
7. P. A. Chapple and W. D. Furneaux, "Changes of Personality in Pregnancy and Labour," *Proceedings of the Royal Society of Medicine*, 1964, *57*, 260-261.
8. D. Breen, *The Birth of a First Child* (London: Tavistock Publications, 1975).
9. A. J. Ferreira, "The Pregnant Mother's Emotional Attitude and Its Reflection upon the Newborn," *American Journal of Orthopsychiatry*, 1960, *30*, 553-561.
10. L. W. Sontag, "The Significance of Fetal Environmental Differences," *American Journal of Obstetrics and Gynecology*, 1941, *42*, 996-1003.

3 The Delivery: When and Where

1. H. F. R. Prechtl, "Behavioural State Cycles in Abnormal Infants," *Developmental Medicine and Child Neurology*, 1973, *15*, 606-615.
2. K. Greene, "The Psychological Effects on Women of the Induction of Labour" (unpublished dissertation, University of Cambridge, 1974).
3. S. Kitzinger, "Some Mothers' Experiences of Induced Labour" (submission to the Department of Health and Social Security from the National Childbirth Trust, 1975).
4. Kitzinger, "Some Mothers' Experiences of Induced Labour."
5. G. J. Kloosterman, "Obstetrics in the Netherlands: A Survival or a Challenge?" (paper presented at Tunbridge Wells Meeting on Problems in Obstetrics organized by the Medical Information Unit of the Spastics Society, 1975).
6. N. Newton, "Mice Delivery in Known and Unfamiliar Environments" (paper presented to the Nineteenth Congress of Psychology, London, 1969).

4 Pain and Relief

1. M. Mead and N. Newton, "Cultural Patterning of Perinatal Behavior." In S. A. Richardson and A. F. Guttmacher, eds., *Childbearing, Its Social and Psychological Aspects* (Baltimore: Williams and Wilkins, in press).
2. E. Marais, *The Soul of the Ape* (Harmondsworth: Penguin, 1973).
3. P. J. Tomlin, "Pethidine Compared with Pethidine Plus Levall-

orphan, and Sterile Water," *British Journal of Anaesthesia*, 1965, *37*, 23-28.
4. L. Chertok, *Psychosomatic Methods in Painless Childbirth* (Oxford: Pergamon Press, 1959).
5. J. W. Scanlon, "Neurobehavioral Responses of Newborn Infants after Maternal Epidural Anesthesia," *Anesthesiology*, 1974, *40(2)*, 121-128.
6. P. J. Tomlin, "Pethidine Compared with Pethidine Plus Levallorphan, and Sterile Water."
7. T. B. Brazelton, "Effect of Prenatal Drugs on the Behavior of the Neonate," *American Journal of Psychiatry*, 1973, *126*, 1261-1266.
8. G. Stechler, "Newborn Attention as Affected by Medication During Labour," *Science*, 1964, *144*, 315-317.
9. Y. Brackbill et al., "Obstetric Meperidine Usage and Assessment of Neonatal Status," *Anesthesiology*, 1974, *40*, 116-120. E. Carway and Y. Brackbill, "Delivery Medication and Infant Outcome: An Empirical Study." In W. A. Bowes et al., eds., *Effects of Obstetrical Medication on the Fetus and Infant* (Monograph of the Society for Research in Child Development No. 35, 1970).
10. M. P. M. Richards and J. F. Bernal, "An Observational Study of Mother-Infant Interaction." In N. Blurton Jones, ed., *Ethological Studies of Child Behaviour* (New York and Cambridge: Cambridge University Press, 1974).
11. S. Turner and J. A. Macfarlane, "Auditory Localization in the Newborn Infant and the Effects of Pethidine," *Developmental Medicine and Child Neurology* (in press).
12. G. Dick-Read, *Childbirth Without Fear* (first published 1933; London: Heinemann Medical Books, 1968; 4th ed., New York: Harper and Row, 1972).
13. S. Kitzinger, *The Experience of Childbirth*, 3rd ed. (Harmondsworth and New York: Penguin, 1972).
14. Chertok, *Psychosomatic Methods in Painless Childbirth*.

5 The First Minutes

1. H. M. Klaus and J. Kennell, "Human Maternal Behaviour at First Contact with Her Young," *Pediatrics*, 1970, *46(2)*, 187-192.
2. K. S. Robson and H. A. Moss, "Patterns and Determinants of Maternal Attachment," *Journal of Pediatrics*, 1970, *77*, 976-985.
3. J. Grey, C. Cutler, J. Dean, and C. H. Kempe, "The Denver Predictive Study from the National Center for the Prevention and Treatment of Child Abuse and Neglect" (unpublished paper, University of Colorado Medical Center).
4. M. Wertheimer, "Psychomotor Coordination of Auditory-Visual

Space at Birth," *Science*, 1961, *134*, 1692.
5. F. Leboyer, *Birth Without Violence* (New York: Alfred A. Knopf, 1975; London: Wildwood House, 1975).
6. W. J. Henneborn and R. Cogan, "The Effect of Husband Participation on Reported Pain and the Probability of Medication During Labour and Birth," *Journal of Psychosomatic Research*, 1975, *19*, 215-222.
7. M. Greenberg and N. Morris, "Engrossment: A Newborn's Impact on the Father," *Journal of Orthopsychiatry*, 1974, *44*, 520-531.

6 What the Baby Knows

1. P. H. Wolff, "Observations on the Development of Smiling." In B. M. Foss, ed., *Determinants of Infant Behaviour*, 2 (London: Methuen, 1963).
2. H. F. R. Prechtl and D. Beintema, "Neurological Examination of the Full-Term Newborn Infant," *Clinics in Developmental Medicine No. 12* (London: Spastics International Medical Publications and Heinemann, 1964). S. J. Hutt et al., "Influence of 'State' upon Responsivity to Stimulation." In S. J. Hutt and C. Hutt, eds., *Early Human Development* (Oxford: Oxford University Press, 1973).
3. J. A. Macfarlane and P. Harris, "Central and Peripheral Vision in Early Infancy," *Journal of Experimental Psychology*, 1976, *21(3)*, 532-538.
4. H. F. R. Prechtl, "Problems of Behavioural Studies in the Newborn Infant." In D. S. Lehoman, R. A. Hinde, and E. Shaw, eds., *Advances in the Study of Behaviour* (New York and London: Academic Press, 1965).
5. R. L. Fantz, "The Origins of Form Perception," *Scientific American*, 1961, *204*, 66-72.
6. R. L. Fantz et al., "Early Visual Selectivity." In L. B. Cohen and P. Salapatek, eds., *Infant Perception: From Sensation to Cognition*, 1 (New York and London: Academic Press, 1975).
7. A. M. Slater and J. M. Findlay, "Binocular Fixation in the Newborn," *Journal of Experimental Child Psychology*, 1975, *20*, 248.
8. T. G. R. Bower, *Development in Infancy* (San Francisco: W. H. Freeman, 1974).
9. G. Carpenter, "Mother's Face and the Newborn," *New Scientist*, 21 March 1974, 742-744.
10. M. Wertheimer, "Psychomotor Coordination of Auditory-Visual Space at Birth," *Science*, 1961, *134*, 1692.
11. S. J. Hutt, "Auditory Discrimination at Birth." In S. J. Hutt and C. Hutt, eds., *Early Human Development*.

12. M. Mills, "Recognition of Mother's Voice in Early Infancy," *Nature*, 1974.
13. X. Turkewitz et al., "Effects of Intensity of Auditory Stimulation on Directional Eye Movements in the Human Neonate," *Animal Behaviour*, 1966, *14*, 93-101.
14. W. Condon, "Speech Makes Babies Move," *New Scientist*, 6 June 1974, 624-627.
15. T. Engen, L. P. Lipsitt, and H. Kay, "Olfactory Responses and Adaptation in the Human Neonate," *Journal of Comparative Physiology and Psychology*, 1963, *56*, 3-5.
16. J. A. Macfarlane, "Olfaction in the Development of Social Preferences in the Human Neonate." In *Parent-Infant Interaction* (Amsterdam: CIBA Foundation Symposium 33, new series, ASP, 1975).
17. K. Crook and L. P. Lipsitt, "Neonatal Nutritive Sucking: Effects of Taste Stimulation upon Sucking Rhythm and Heart Rate," *Child Development*, 1976, *47*, 518-522.
18. P. Johnson and D. M. Salisbury, "Breathing and Sucking During Feeding in the Newborn." In *Parent-Infant Interaction* (Amsterdam: CIBA Foundation Symposium 33, new series, ASP, 1975).
19. J. F. Bernal, "Crying During the First Ten Days and Maternal Responses," *Developmental Medicine and Child Neurology*, 1972, *14*, 362.
20. M. P. M. Richards, J. F. Bernal, and Y. Brackbill, "Early Behavioural Differences: Gender or Circumcision," *Developmental Psychobiology*, 1976, *9*, 89-95.
21. J. A. Ambrose, discussion contribution in J. A. Ambrose, ed., *Stimulation in Early Infancy* (New York and London: Academic Press, 1970).

7 Mother and Child: Separation

1. H. J. Kennell et al., "Evidence for a Sensitive Period in the Human Mother." In *Parent-Infant Interaction* (Amsterdam: CIBA Foundation Symposium 33, new series, ASP, 1975).
2. M. Klaus et al., "Maternal Attachment: Importance of the First Post-Partum Days," *New England Journal of Medicine*, 1972, *286*, 460.
3. H. J. Kennell et al., "Maternal Behaviour One Year after Early and Extended Post Partum Contact," *Developmental Medicine and Child Neurology*, 1974, *16*(2), 172-179.
4. A. Whiten, "Postnatal Separation and Mother-Infant Interaction" (paper presented at the Conference of the International Society for the Study of Behavioural Development, University of Surrey,

1975). M. J. Seashore et al., "The Effects of Denial of Early Mother-Infant Interaction on Maternal Self-Confidence," *Journal of Personality and Social Psychology*, 1973 *26*(*3*), 369-378.

5. A. M. Lynch, "Ill-Health and Child Abuse," *The Lancet*, 16 August 1975, 317.

6. D. H. Scott, "Follow-up Study from Birth of the Effects of Prenatal Stresses," *Developmental Medicine and Child Neurology*, 1973, *15*, 770-787.

7. A. Blake, A. Stewart, and D. Turcan, "Parents of Babies of Very Low Birth Weight." In *Parent-Infant Interaction*.

8 Mother and Child: Socialization

1. I. E. Eibl-Eibesfeldt, *Love and Hate* (London: Methuen, 1971).

2. B. Garner and L. Wallach, "Shapes of Figures Identified as a Baby's Head," *Perceptual and Motor Skills*, 1965, *20*, 135-142.

3. I. E. Eibl-Eibesfeldt, *Ethology: The Biology of Behavior* (New York: Holt, Rinehart and Winston, 1970).

4. K. S. Robson and H. A. Moss, "Patterns and Determinants of Maternal Attachment," *Journal of Pediatrics*, 1970, *77*, 976-985.

5. J. Newson, "Towards a Theory of Infant Understanding," *Bulletin of the British Psychological Society*, 1974, *27*, 251-257.

6. H. S. Bennett, "Infant-Caretaker Interactions," *Journal of American Child Psychiatry*, 1971, *10*(*2*).

7. Newson, "Towards a Theory of Infant Understanding."

8. P. P. G. Bateson, "The Imprinting of Birds." In S. A. Barnett, ed., "Ethology and Development," *Clinics in Developmental Medicine No. 47* (London: Spastics International Medical Publications and Heinemann, 1973).

9. L. S. Sander et al., "Early Mother-Infant Interaction and Twenty-Four-Hour Patterns of Activity and Sleep," *Journal of the American Academy of Child Psychiatry*, 1970, *9*, 103.

10. D. Levy, *Behavioral Analysis* (Springfield, Ill.: Thomas, 1958).

11. Sander et al., "Early Mother-Infant Interaction and Twenty-Four-Hour Patterns of Activity and Sleep."

12. T. J. Gaensbauer and R. N. Emde, "Wakefulness and Feeding in Human Newborns," *Archives of General Psychiatry*, 1973, *28*, 894-897.

13. H. R. Schaffer, ed., *Interactions in Infancy* (New York and London: Academic Press, in press).

14. J. F. Bernal, "Consistency and Change in Maternal Style." In *Parent-Infant Interaction* (Amsterdam: CIBA Foundation Symposium 33, new series, ASP, 1975).

Suggested Reading

Dana Breen, *The Birth of a First Child* (London: Tavistock Publications, 1975). Interesting but fairly complex and technical results of an in-depth psychological examination of
fifty women experiencing late pregnancy and early moth-
erhood for the first time; worth the effort it demands.

Geraldine Flanagan, *The First Nine Months of Life* (New York:
Simon and Schuster, 1962; London: Heinemann Medical
Books, 1963). A fairly detailed account of how the fetus
develops in the uterus. It includes a number of color
photos of fetuses at different stages, together with se-
quences of shots showing movement in response to touch.

Sheila Kitzinger, *The Experience of Childbirth*, 3rd ed. (Harmondsworth and New York: Penguin, 1972). A fine and
very popular introduction to Sheila Kitzinger's own
method of preparation for birth, which involves not only
understanding of the physiology of birth and acquain-
tanceship with relaxation and breathing techniques, but
also acceptance of birth as part of a woman's sexual
development.

Sheila Kitzinger and John Davies, eds., *The Place of Birth* (Oxford: Oxford University Press, in press). A fascinating
collection of papers on the advantages and disadvantages
of home and hospital delivery. Not particularly easy to
read but an important book.

Raven Lang, *The Birth Book* (Palo Alto, Calif.: Science and Behavior Books, 1972). Some fascinating descriptions by a
group of people involved, despite legal prohibition, in
home deliveries in the state of California. The book
shows some of the alternatives open to people with this
kind of determination.

Frederick Leboyer, *Birth Without Violence* (New York: Alfred
A. Knopf, 1975; London: Wildwood House, 1975). The
rationale behind this French obstetrician's novel approach
to delivery; brief, illustrated, distinctly poetic for a book
on this topic, and certainly rather compelling.

Roger Lewin, ed., *Child Alive* (New York: Doubleday, 1975; London: Temple-Smith, 1975). A substantial collection of extremely readable articles by a number of leading researchers in child development; an excellent introduction to the surprising competence of small babies.

M. P. M. Richards, ed., *The Integration of the Child into a Social World* (Cambridge: Cambridge University Press, 1974). Another collection of papers, but at a much higher level. It raises a number of tough but interesting issues concerned with the question of how human beings become social.

Index

Credits

Date Due

DEC 2 '77	Apr. 3rd		MAY 11 1995
MAR 20 78	SEP 22 '82		
MAY 25 '78	DEC 12 '84		
JUN 2 78	NOV 29 '90		
NOV 17 '78			
DEC 22 78	APR 14 1994		
MAY 18 79			
NOV 21 80			
NOV 17 80			
MAR 20 81			

WITHDRAWN

WITHDRAWN